Introduction

The production of this book is a bit of a first in the domestic, pure-bred poultry world. The Buying Guide approach we adopt in *Practical Poultry* magazine is unique, and I know that each one we publish gives the breed featured a significant boost, both in terms of general awareness and potential ownership interest.

Now, for the first time, poultry enthusiasts have the chance to own a selection of these comprehensive features in a single, convenient, bound volume. I'm hoping that it'll prove to be a popular seller, not just from a commercial point of view, but because making the right choice about the breed of bird you buy is so fundamentally important.

All too many keepers, especially those new to the hobby, still tend to buy on looks alone. Now, while this may be a significant factor from an aesthetic point of view, it can pale into insignificance compared to the more practical issues which will govern day-to-day life with the birds.

Factors such as temperament, flightiness, laying ability, susceptibility to parasites and disease, ease of handling and space requirements are vital considerations all too often ignored by over-keen buyers. People who rush in to the purchase process, buying on a whim, typically make mistakes, ending up with birds that ultimately prove unsuitable to their situation.

The articles in this book should be regarded as practical guides, and used in conjunction with additional feedback gained from breed specialists. The relevant breed clubs are easy to contact (many have websites), and I strongly recommend purchasers more money than sourcing birds from a local sale or market, you'll almost certainly end up with better, healthier stock, which is the name of the game!

The core purpose of this book is to help potential purchasers recognise good birds from bad ones. Consequently, the guides have been written with the requirements of the official breed standards in mind, thus pointing buyers towards the best possible examples in each case. Although it's obviously not essential to have exhibition-quality chickens in your back garden, there's certainly no point in knowingly buying sub-standard examples; after all, they'll cost you just as much to feed!

Chris Graham
Editor,
Practical Poultry *magazine*

Published by
KELSEY PUBLISHING LTD
Printed by Wyndeham Heron on behalf of
Kelsey Publishing Ltd, Cudham Tithe Barn, Berry's Hill, Cudham, Kent TN16 3AG
Tel: 01959 541444   *Fax:* 01959 541400   *Email:* kelseybooks@kelsey.co.uk   *Website:* www.kelsey.co.uk

©2009 **ISBN 978-1-873098-95-0**

Choosing Your Chickens

16

CONTENTS

158

67

21

74

122

47

Andalusian

Praise to the Andalusian – a really useful breed that's strangely out of fashion

A The comb is one of the Andalusian's most distinctive features. It should be folded like this on the female (to about eye-level), but upright and deeply serrated on the male.

B The eye should be prominent and coloured dark red or red-brown. Those which appear too light are best avoided.

C Face should be smooth, free from feathers and bright red on both male and female birds. White on the face is a serious failure point.

D In common with other Mediterranean breeds, the Andalusian's ear lobe should be pure white, with no traces of red or pink. Ideally it should be almond-shaped and smooth with no creases.

E Neck should be long, gracefully curved and well covered with hackle feathers that are glossy black on both male and female birds. Red or yellow in the hackles is a serious fault.

F The grey-blue ground colour and black lacing to most feathers are key features of the Andalusian. Both aspects can be controlled by careful selection and breeding, but it's not easy breeding to exhibition standard.

G Tail is held reasonably upright on both males and females. Sickle feathers on the male should be lustrous black, to match the saddle and hackle feathers.

H Wings are relatively long and held tight to the body. Being a 'light breed', the Andalusian is a flier, and will easily flutter over most normal garden hedges or fences. Containment can be an issue for urban dwellers.

I There should be four straight and evenly-spread toes on each foot, all free from feathers.

J Legs are long and contribute to the bird's 'reachy' look. Shanks should be free from feathers and slate grey or black.

K A full and rounded breast is important, with a covering of distinctly laced feathers.

L Wattles should be long and finely textured – larger on the male.

M Beak needs to be stout, medium length and predominantly slate coloured; some horn colouring is acceptable.

With its 'reachy', Game-like type and very attractive plumage colouring, the Andalusian will grace any garden. This male has a reasonable head, but is lacking lacing definition and black sickles. Well-marked examples are few and far between these days

One of the biggest mysteries connected with the rare Andalusian is why it continues to remain so rare! For a breed that has so much going for it, it's strange that it's kept by so few keepers; even at the UK's premier poultry shows, you'll be lucky to see more than a handful of these striking birds on display.

So what's the problem? Does the name sound too foreign? Are people put off by an image of unmanageable Mediterranean temperament? Or perhaps it's simply that the breed has fallen to such a degree that nowadays it's hard to learn about, and even harder to buy.

Whatever the reason, the dwindling numbers are a crying shame, and would-be keepers are missing a great opportunity. The Andalusian offers cracking overall appearance, very attractive plumage colouring on both male and female birds, plus all the utility performance you could reasonably want from a pure breed. Yet despite having been around for well over 100 years in more or less its present form – and a bantam version being available too – these pretty birds are forced to languish on the periphery of the poultry Fancy, without a dedicated club to support and promote them.

Spanish roots?

Like so many of our 'traditional' pure breeds, when you start digging into the Andalusian's background, the waters very quickly become muddied! Popular belief has it that the breed was originally developed in south-western Spain, in a region around Cadiz called Andalusia – but this isn't strictly true. Certainly, Spanish fowl from that area were used as a starting point, but most evidence suggests that the significant breeding and development work was carried out in England, by a handful of enthusiasts during the late 1800s. So the attractive bird we have today is, essentially, a man-made creation, and certainly isn't a native fowl of Southern Spain!

The actual dates involved are a little vague as well, but it seems that the Andalusian's forbears arrived in the UK during the late 1840s, either brought here by

Spanish traders or imported directly to order by enthusiast breeders. By all accounts, these first birds were a bit of a mixed bag, with most being either black or white, and just a few presenting blueish/slate grey plumage. Their colourings were apparently somewhat drab and plain too, with little sign of the attractive two-tone or lacing effects seen on today's version. However, the early breeders obviously recognised some potential there, and must have fancied the look of the few grey examples they'd bought.

Once again, precise records of the development work don't exist, and so the crossing combinations used vary according to which printed history you read. It's commonly thought, though, that the Spanish was the first breed to be worked into the genetic mix, with some suggesting that this was to introduce the folded comb on the female. Careful selection was obviously made in favour of any dark lacing which appeared, although one contemporary report suggests that at some point birds were produced with light-coloured lacing! It seems that the Minorca played a part too, perhaps to increase the size of the comb and bring in greater weight to the dark lacing. There's also a suggestion that blue Old English Game – very popular at the time in Devon and Cornwall – were used as crosses, and that this was the source of the Andalusian's now characteristic 'reachiness'. This, presumably, would have also enhanced the blue feathering and endowed the emerging breed with additional visual grace and practical hardiness.

Careful selection from then on must have been responsible for developing the Andalusian's Game-like appearance further, by favouring breeding birds which stood tall, showed a slender body and an alert, active character. Fortunately, though, this process wasn't responsible for any significant loss in the breed's fundamental vitality. It remained (and still is today) a strong and hardy bird. Sexual vigour is still good, as are fertility levels, and the resultant youngsters generally develop quickly and strongly.

Legs should be long, featherless and dark

Hey, good looking!

Officially classified as a Light Breed, the Andalusian is characterised by its upright, bold and active nature. It's a bird with graceful lines yet broad shoulders. Its feathering is close and compact, and both sexes show a well-rounded, full breast. The wings are long (it is a flier!) and held close to the body, while the tail is reasonably upright but not fanned.

The male's head is dominated by a good-sized, upright and deeply serrated single comb that's balanced by long, thin wattles. The face is red as well, but the almond-shaped ear lobes should be pure white, smooth and uncreased. In the best examples, these bright lobes create a striking contrast with the red headgear which, itself, should all be fine-textured and smooth.

The female presents similar head colouring, although everything is smaller as you'd expect and, most significantly, the comb falls to one side, with a single fold. Both sexes stand on long legs that should be either slate grey or black. The shanks and feet must be free from

Ground colour evenness and lacing consistency are key aspects for an exhibition standard bird. However, a lack of perfection isn't really an issue if you aren't involved with showing and are simply keeping the birds as backyard fowl

inevitable be producing a high proportion of 'redundant' stock, as the blacks and whites only need to be used occasionally in a breeding program to tweak certain aspects of the blue's appearance.

Good prospect?

The Andalusian probably enjoyed its popularity heyday during the early 1900s, when it was quite widely kept as both an exhibition and utility fowl. In those days, of course, poultry had to earn its keep in all but the most affluent situations and the Andalusian, like the other Mediterranean breeds, was recognised as a good layer of large, flavoursome, white-shelled eggs.

So its gradual fall from grace is difficult to fathom. There have been breed clubs for it in the past, but nothing very recently. Without a specialist club, and the camaraderie among like-minded enthusiasts that this tends to generate, a breed's profile diminishes. Fashions change too, although I can't really imagine that such an attractive and useful bird could become a victim in this way. Maybe the answer lies in the breeding difficulties; who knows?

But things are as they are, and the current rarity of the Andalusian means that sourcing good stock is likely to be a bit of a struggle. Without a dedicated club to look after its interests, the Andalusian falls under the protective umbrella of the Rare Poultry Society, so this is where any search should begin. It's important always to buy the best stock you can get your hands on – with this breed or any other. However, if you have any ambitions to show in the future, then you really must seek out an experienced and recommended breeder via the RPS, and buy the best birds that you can reasonably afford. Even if you're not into the exhibition scene, there really is no point in knowingly settling for poor quality.

Unfortunately, with the number of quality breeders around today being almost countable on the fingers of one hand, the odds are rather stacked against you from the start. Add to this the fact that really good, well-laced examples are very difficult to find at the moment, and you'll start to appreciate what

Breeding blue Andalusians produces a proportion of 'splash' offspring, like these two. This colour can be used to tackle 'sootiness' in the blue's ground colour as part of a breeding program. Other than that, splash birds are generally surplus to an exhibitor's requirements, but they represent an attractive and equally productive option for the backyard keeper

feathers, with four straight and well-spaced toes.

As far as colour is concerned, the standardised version of the Andalusian is the blue. In reality, of course, this 'blueness' often tends to be in the eye of the beholder, with most birds looking fundamentally grey with just a hint of blue. However, much of this breed's beauty comes from its feather lacing; most feathers on these birds should be fringed with a reasonably wide edging of black, creating a wonderful contrast with the blue/grey ground colour.

The exceptions to this include the male's neck hackle, saddle and sickle feathers, all of which should be a rich, glossy black. Black feathers like this on the female are restricted to the neck hackles.

Lacing quality, however, is a serious breeding issue these days, with many birds (including some of those illustrated here) failing to reach the required standard.

Producing a top-quality blue Andalusian is no easy task. As with any 'blue' breed, the desired effect is produced by the careful crossing of the black and white colour genes. Then, when mating the blue offspring together, the chicks produced follow a formula first noted by Gregor Mendel, the 'father of genetics'. Only half of the hatchlings will have the blue plumage of their parents; of the remaining 50%, 25% will be black and 25% will be white ('splash', which is white with random dark mottling). This means that those seeking to breed for exhibition will

you're up against. But, the good news is that getting your birds is likely to be the greatest struggle that the Andalusian keeper will have to face.

In practical terms, keeping and caring for this attractive breed couldn't really be simpler. These birds really don't demand any special conditions over and above the normal good husbandry issues. The Andalusian is a hardy breed that'll happily endure most climates other than the extremes. They can adapt to free-range or confined lifestyles but, given the opportunity, will be enthusiastic and active foragers.

Healthy hens will come into lay as early as February, and their productive season will extend right through to late October or early November, and birds from a good strain should produce 180+ eggs over that period. However, being a light breed means that the Andalusian tends towards flightiness, but the best way to tackle this – if you're hatching your own birds – is to handle the chicks regularly from day one. With adult birds, much will depend on the strain, and how they've been reared. The flightiest examples will need to be contained. While they're unlikely to fly off into nearby trees, they will certainly be capable of fluttering over fences and hedges up to about six feet high. Bear this in mind if you live in an urban

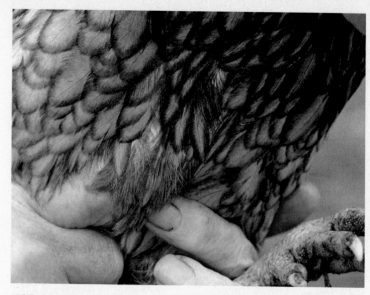

While not a problem from a utility point of view, this is typical of the sort of sub-standard lacing that would represent a serious failing in the eyes of a show judge

environment. Wing clipping is an option you could consider, but only if you're not intending to exhibit the birds.

Breeding-on with bought-in stock is an interesting business. It's all about balancing the breeding pair to give yourself the best chance of quality offspring. One experienced breeder suggested to me that light blue males are best paired-up with dark blue females (assuming both are showing good,

defined lacing), and *vice versa*. From an exhibition point of view, half the points available to a bird are dependent on ground colour (30pts) and lacing quality (20pts), so these are crucial aspects. Get the breeding balance wrong, though, and both the quality of the lacing and the ground colour can quickly be lost and, with them, much of the essence of the bird.

The Andalusian is a breed most certainly in need of, and deserving, a great deal more support. Its inexplicable tumble into relative obscurity flies in the face of all the positive aspects the bird has to offer – hardiness, beauty, adaptability, ruggedness and practicality. If your taste is for a chicken that's graceful, productive and visually distinctive, then the Andalusian is the breed for you. •

Male Andalusians should have matching glossy black colouring on hackle, saddle and sickle feathers. This bird is lacking in the tail department

YES OR NO?
✔ Good layer.
✔ Simple to keep.
✔ Hardy.
✔ Attractive show bird.
✔ Tasty to eat.

✘ Flighty.
✘ Difficult to locate good stock.

Australorp

A good Australorp can offer an essentially trouble-free source of eggs and interest whatever the keeper's level of experience

Although the Australorp is officially listed as having its origins in Great Britain, this doesn't quite do justice to the real situation; namely, the pivotal role played in its development by dedicated and skilful breeders in Australia during the early 1900s.

The original intention behind the Orpington, created in 1886 by William Cook and named after the Kentish town where he lived, was to produce the perfect all-rounder; a heavy, soft-feathered bird offering top-drawer utility performance (plenty of eggs and meat). Cook also set out to create a bird that was both hardy and attractive, and achieved all this with a careful breeding program involving black Minorca males and black Langshan females, the black offspring from which were then crossed with the black Plymouth Rock.

The final result, the black Orpington, was a great success, with exports speeding off all round the world. But it was breeders in Australia who, with an eye on the commercial egg-producing market, set about the development of the breed even further. A carefully-managed breeding program over a 25-year period proved successful, with laying trials establishing that the bird was up there with the very best; some stories suggest that the top strain laid 350+ eggs in a season!

Welcome 'home'

Then, during the 1920s, the Australorp (the name created simply by combining 'Australian'

Above: the blue Australorp is arguably the prettiest of the three colours

and 'Orpington') started filtering back to the UK. By that stage, the original Orpington had become a popular show bird in Britain, and had been extensively crossed with breeds such as the Cochin, to enhance its size and overall feathering. This process of 'fancification' had effectively robbed the Orpington of its practical usefulness as a utility bird, so the arrival of the Australorp caused quite a stir.

A club was quickly formed to support the breed, and appreciative keepers began revelling in the fact that they could once again own a bird with the presence and attractiveness of the original Orpington, and one that offered genuinely useful utility qualities too.

A black bantam version was created during the 1940s, to meet the wartime need for manageable, productive small fowl for the domestic keeper. White bantam and large fowl versions followed, although the latter disappeared again. In more recent times, an attractive blue bantam was developed (during the 1980s) and was followed, a decade or so later, by a blue large fowl. What's more, the club has plans to re-create a standardised white large fowl version soon too.

Today the bantam remains the firm favourite among the 130 members of the Australorp Club, with enthusiasts of the large fowl being relatively few and far between. Both bantam and large fowl versions lay well, although not up to the high standards set during the Australian laying trials. Nevertheless, keepers of

A This is a young female so her comb isn't fully developed or coloured yet. However, the requirement is for a good, straight, single, upright comb that, ideally, will feature no more than seven serrations – more do occur. The comb is correspondingly smaller on the female, and should never be so large that it falls to either side.

B A good Australorp will always have a prominent large and dark eye. Ideally, black is best, meaning that it's all but impossible to distinguish any colour difference between the pupil and the iris. A dark brown iris is acceptable, but nothing lighter than that. A red or orange eye is bad news, and can be a tell-tale indicator that the bird is not purebred.

C Pay particular attention to the colour of the ear lobes when buying Australorps. These should be as red as possible, and any white seen here is regarded as a serious fault on birds destined for the show pen. Most typically it can be a problem with bantam whites and blues, but it can be found (less frequently) on large blacks too.

D The Australorp's face should be bright red, free from feathers and smooth. Birds that show black in the face are best avoided if you're interested in showing, and shouldn't be used as breeding stock. If you are simply after back garden hens then of course this isn't an issue.

E Beak colour does vary with plumage. On black birds like this one it is important that it's as dark as possible, in keeping with the eye and legs. Black is most desirable, although some degree of horn colouring is tolerated. Blue Australorps should show a blue or black beak, although again some horn colour is tolerated.

F The Australorp's back should be both wide and flat.

G Male birds tend to hold their tails at a higher angle than the females, although it's important that hens don't allow theirs to fall flat; an appreciable angle between tail and back, like this, is a good thing to look for.

H Australorp hens can have a tendency to run to fat if they're fed over-enthusiastically and/or kept in close confinement. Consequently, the feeding of dietary treats and supplements needs to be carefully regulated. An overweight hen can be identified by the presence of fatty deposits around the rump and vent area, which can be felt during handling.

I It's important that fluff levels are minimal on the Australorp. Feathering generally should be tighter than on the Orpington, and the presence of excessive feathering on the thighs and around the rear end is a bad sign that's likely to indicate a sub-standard layer.

J Legs should be dark slate/blue grey or black. Note that there is a tendency for this colouring to fade as the bird gets older. All should be free from feather.

K Bent toes can be a problem in poor strains, so inspect feet carefully. Also, check the colour of the underside of the feet. The best birds will show very pale or white colouring here. Poor examples can be obviously pink, or even green, and are best avoided.

L The wings are held tight to the body. When buying, spread wings carefully to check for abnormally coloured feathers; white on the blacks can be a problem and should be avoided in young birds. Don't breed from birds showing incorrect feather colours. All black feathers must have a good, beetle-green sheen, not a purple one. However, if you spot a purple/blue barring in the feathers, this is likely to have been caused by an upset in feather growth, and isn't a problem.

M The breast should be deep, full and rounded – but not bulging. When handling the bird, always check that the breast bone feels straight. If you're buying large fowl then take time to assess overall weight. There is a bit of a tendency for these birds to be a little on the light side these days.

Above: *A good eye should be almost solid black, so that it's virtually impossible to differentiate between the pupil and the iris. This young female has a good beak colour too*

Left: *In show birds, white in the ear lobe is a fault to watch for, as is 'fishtailing' in the comb – here, spikes three and four (counting from the back) are 'joined' so the pair resemble a fish-tail shape*

young, healthy hens should expect around 200 good-sized, tinted eggs a year.

But part of the charm of the Australorp is its straightforward beauty! Not only is the breed practical and easy to keep, but it's genuinely attractive too. All versions have a graceful look to them, presenting an upright yet active stance. The body shape is deep and broad, with a well-rounded breast and compact tail. The wings are relatively small, and held tight to the body, and the bird stands on clean, well-spaced and strong legs.

The most popular Australorp, the black, should feature a characteristic, beetle-green sheen, particularly apparent when the feathers catch the sun. The all-over, rich black feathering contrasts wonderfully with the bright red face, wattles, ear lobes and single comb. The eyes should be large and dark (black if possible), as should the beak, legs and feet. The attractive blue version should feature very dark grey neck hackles, saddle, wing bows and tail, but slate blue everywhere else, with single dark lacing around the edges of these lighter feathers. As with the black, the face and headgear

must be bright red, and the beak, legs and feet as dark as possible.

Gentle friends

As far as character is concerned, the Australorp retains many of the Orpington's most endearing traits. These birds are docile, quiet, friendly and easy-going. While they love to freerange, they are happy in confinement too, assuming they're not over-crowded or allowed to run

Always spread the wings of birds you intent buying, to check for uniform feather colouring. Note how blacks have this very characteristic beetle-green sheen

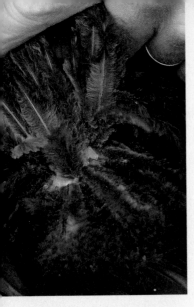

Undercolour should be as even as possible, right down to the light-coloured skin

Legs should be as dark as possible. Toe nails, as with the underside of the feet, are white on the best examples

to fat. This makes them just about the perfect family bird, particularly considering their very worthwhile laying ability. Add to this their white skin and generally well-fleshed body that can make a tasty roast, and you surely have the sort of practical all-rounder that William Cook had been striving for all those years ago.

The generally relaxed manner of the Australorp makes it easy to look after, even for novice keepers. Although the bantams can be a little flightier than the large fowl versions, the breed is not known as a flier so pen security isn't a big issue for owners living in more urban environments. There are no special husbandry requirements associated with this breed, and its impressive hardiness means that

general resistance to the range of common poultry diseases is very good. What's more, the best strains of these birds also tend to enjoy a high level of inherent resistance to physical deformities, such as bent toes or twisted beaks.

The no-nonsense aspect to the Australorp means that the breed will live quite happily on a straightforward diet of layers pellets or mash supplemented, if you wish, with a mixed corn scratch feed in the afternoons. Be careful, though, if your birds aren't able to free range, as there can be a tendency for hens to run to fat, particularly in their second year. If you allow this to happen then not only will it have potentially serious health implications for the birds, but it will also adversely affect their laying ability and general levels of fertility.

For those interested in breeding, the news is very encouraging too. Australorp hens make good broody birds that sit reliably and go on to be attentive mothers once the chicks have hatched. The young birds themselves also tend to be strong, and rarely seem to suffer with any sort of growing-related problem. In fact, just about the most serious Australorp-related problem you'll encounter is the struggle involved in sourcing good stock, especially if you're after large fowl. As always, we recommend contacting the breed club in the first instance. This is certainly the best way of starting your search as the country's best breeders are among the 130 members. If you want to keep Australorps that perform well and look good too, then you must buy birds from a good strain. Those which have been crossed with Orpingtons or Cochins in their recent history – for whatever reason – may well appear visually stunning, but are likely to be somewhat lacking when it comes to egg production. So, as always, do your research – speak to and, if possible, visit the breeder you intend buying from. Ask lots of questions and if you detect any reluctance or confusion in the answers, then simply walk away. Buy from an established and recognised breeder and you'll secure yourself a superb bird that'll provide years of practical pleasure. •

The white Australorp bantam is an attractive option; large fowl whites are on their way, too. The Australorp is an easy and productive breed to keep

Barnevelder

If you're searching for a robust, low-maintenance yet attractive and friendly egg layer, then you need look no further than the Dutch Barnevelder

K

J

I

Barnevelder eggs as dark as the three darker ones shown here are a rarity these days. Breeding for the exhibition pen means the intensity of shell colour has been lost in many strains

H

F

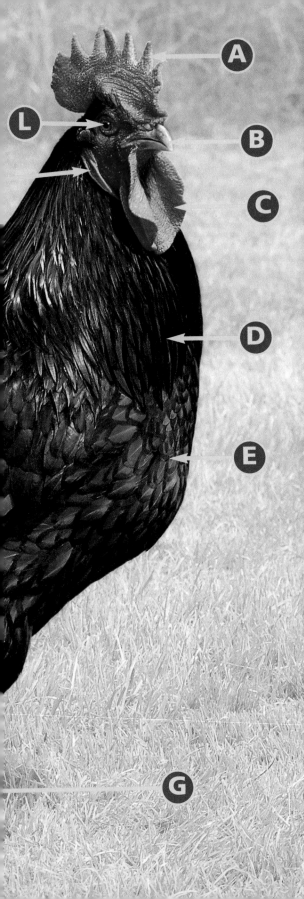

A Male Barnevelders like this should ideally have five upright points on their single comb. Any sign of side sprigs is a bad thing, so avoid this when buying. Hens have much smaller combs, but these still need to be well formed and smooth (not crinkly).

B The beak should be short, full and yellow-coloured – sometimes with a darker area at the tip. The rare silver variety has more of a horn-coloured beak.

C The medium-sized wattles should be bright red like this, matching the colour of the comb, ear lobes and feather-free face.

D Male birds should have predominantly black hackle feathering, with a good beetle green sheen when catching the light. These feathers should show contrasting, red-brown shafting.

E Male birds have single-laced feathering on the breast, which needs to be deep and full. Poor quality examples will lack the orange quill, or may even have orange/brown hackle feathers. The Dutch standard requires a black breast on the males. These same feathers are double-laced on the female, with two lines of black on each feather. Watch out for a light, washed-out appearance and for bright yellow shafting on females. These sorts of problems are difficult to pick up on young birds. This can really only be assessed on birds that are six months old or older, and have their adult plumage. Generally dark growers stand the best chance of developing into well-coloured adults.

F The wings are short and tend to be carried tight to the body.

G The legs should be yellow and always free from feathers. There can be a tendency for them to show a black 'dustiness', which is a bad point and should be avoided. It's also worth noting that the yellowness of the legs on females will fade away as the laying season progresses.

H Despite the best efforts of exhibition keepers, the feathering on a good Barnevelder remains quite tight and there isn't too much fluff evident. Watch for white undercolour. A little bit of this is OK, but it shouldn't get out of hand otherwise it'll start creeping into wing tips, etc. It can also occur in cockerels' tails if you're not careful. Generally the undercolour should be slate grey right down to the skin and cockerels will often show a little bit of this colour at the base of their tails.

I Avoid tails that are too upright or lean forwards towards the head (squirrel tail), as well as those which slant to either side when viewed from above (wry tail). Also watch out for, and steer clear of, white feathering in the tail.

J The back should be relatively short, with good birds featuring a graceful U-shaped curve created by the neck, back and tail combination.

K Ear lobes should be bright red with no sign of any white. The latter can be caused by undesirable cross-breeding and should be avoided if birds are to be exhibited.

L The eye should be bold, bright and prominent. You should be looking for a rich, reddy-brown colour, and those which appear light-coloured and washed-out are best avoided.

The Barnevelder is a comparatively new breed which emerged in the early 1920s and is one of the most attractive, unsung heroes of the pure breed commercial poultry world.

It takes its name from the small Dutch town of Barneveld where it was created, and is believed to have resulted from the crossing of local fowl with imported Asiatic breeds – including the Brahma, Langshan and Malay.

The primary objective was to improve the egg-laying performance of the local Dutch hens, and this is exactly what happened. But, as an added bonus, it turned out that the Barnevelder became famous for not only the large size of the egg it produced, but for its wonderful, dark-coloured shell too.

Unfortunately, like all the other traditional utility fowl, the Barnevelder's time in the commercial egg production spotlight was to be short-lived. It fell from grace during the 1950s, in the face of stiff competition from the hybrid layers from America. But the Barnevelder fought on, and found favour among hobby keepers for whom ultimate egg production wasn't of primary importance. The breed's attractive looks and gentle temperament gave it significant appeal at the domestic level, and the particularly attractive double-

A male head with characteristic five-pointed comb, good wattle, face and ear lobe colour, rich eye and stout beak

The yellow leg and foot colour can fade during the season, particularly on hens. Redness on male birds, as here, is acceptable, but black discolouration isn't

laced version drew the attention of exhibitors.

But while interest from the Fancy undoubtedly helped prevent the Barnevelder from slipping into poultry oblivion, there was a price to be paid. Show breeders, as they so often do, took it upon themselves to 'improve' the look of the bird and, in particular, its feathering. While this led to the creation of an arguably more attractive bird, it also had a detrimental effect on both egg quality and numbers. But perhaps the greatest loss was in shell colour, which became somewhat washed-out.

Today the breed remains a popular domestic choice in Holland and elsewhere in mainland Europe. It's a bit more of a rarity in the UK, although is still supported in healthy numbers by a dedicated group of enthusiastic keepers.

Buying options
Currently there are just four standardised Barnevelder colours; black, double-laced, partridge and silver. The black, silver and partridge are all very rare, and it's the double-laced which is by far the most popular and widely kept. There is also a white version (again rare) and some breeders in the UK are attempting to produce a blue-laced version. I've heard reports that this is a very attractive looking bird but, because it's not a standardised colour, it's unlikely to be accepted by the Club.

The Barnevelder is characterised by a broad, deep and full body, with a medium head and red face that's free from feathers. The single comb, wattles and ear lobes are all bright red, and the eyes should be orangey-brown. The bird stands on unfeathered, yellow legs and feet. Male, double-laced birds feature

The patchy, lighter brown colouring on this hen has been caused by the sun. It's only a problem if you intend showing your birds

Barnevelder hens have much smaller combs, wattles and ear lobes, as you would expect

dark hackle feathers (with a beetle-green sheen) with contrasting edging and pronounced red/brown shafting. The breast is red-brown with black lacing, and contrasts with a black tail. The wings are broadly laced with a red-brown bay showing when closed.

The female has black hackles, but much more lacing over the rest of her body – including the tail – than on the male. The black and white types are both solid colour versions, while the partridge presents a combination of black and brown feathering, the latter being tipped with black to create the partridge effect.

These are the characteristic light shafts you should be looking for in a good double-laced male's hackle feathers

While not classified as a rare breed here in the UK, the overall number of Barnevelders is not particularly high, which means that sourcing good stock can be a little trickier than it might be for some of the more numerous breeds. In reality, there are probably only about a handful of breeders producing top quality stock at the moment, and these suppliers are best contacted via the breed club.

Practical proposition

The Barnevelder is a hardy breed; the type of bird that, assuming all the basic welfare requirements are met, can be left largely to its own devices. It's not a 'high maintenance' breed to own and, thanks to its durable nature, resistance to all the usual chicken-related diseases tends to be high. Some breeders report the odd outbreak of coccidiosis among their your stock, but these are rare and that's just about all there is to worry about.

These aspects, and the fact that these birds have a very pleasant relaxed character, and are generally robust, make the Barnevelder an excellent choice for the beginner. They are easy to handle and straightforward to keep; who could ask for more than that? Adverse weather isn't a particular problem and, being a relatively small-winged, heavy breed, flying isn't an issue either – they can be effectively contained with little more than a

four-foot fence in the right environment.

Like most breeds, the Barnevelder enjoys a free-range lifestyle given the chance. But its placid nature means that if confinement is necessary, then this shouldn't be a desperate problem either, assuming, of course, that the birds are not being overcrowded.

Another benefit of their calm nature is that 'Barnies' rarely seem prone to disruptive and destructive vices such as feather pecking or fighting. This isn't to say, however, that these things can't be provoked by poor environment and/or stress, because they certainly can.

If you intend to breed with these birds then this should prove a fairly uneventful process too.

Fertility levels are typically good, as are hatch rates. Consequently, it's rare to hear stories of keepers encountering hatching or rearing problems with this breed. Just about the only potential problem can occur if youngsters are moved out of the brooder too soon, although this isn't a Barnevelder-specific danger. As a guide, experienced breeders don't let their young stock out until about the eight-week old mark, at which point the youngsters should certainly be strong enough to grow-on healthily from there.

One final point with regard to breeding is that Barnie hens certainly don't make good broody mothers. This shouldn't come as any great surprise given the breed's

These double-laced youngsters are about six weeks old. The darker they are at this stage, the more chance there is that they will grow up to be well-marked adults

commercial utility roots. Most of the broody tendency will have been bred-out during the original development process and, although you may find the odd hen displaying broody tendencies, these birds can't generally be relied upon in this respect. So, anyone keen on the natural brooding route will need to bring in a reliable broody hen, such as a Silkie, to incubate and hatch the eggs.

This lack of broodiness is potentially just about the only downside of this much under-rated Dutch breed, and even this won't be an issue for most domestic keepers who either aren't interested in breeding, or use an incubator anyway. Every other aspect of the breed must surely get a resounding thumbs-up. Barnevelders are an attractive, productive and family-friendly breed and, although they can't boast the history of some of our more established pure breeds, they are thoroughly deserving of your support nonetheless. •

A good Barnie hen will show wonderful double-laced feathering over virtually all of her body, apart from the neck hackle

Slate grey undercolour is a double-laced Barnevelder requirement; it's usually slightly darker on male birds

Belgian bearded

Male d'Uccle millefleur, with characteristic single comb and feathered legs

Some of the secrets of picking out good examples of this enchanting true bantam

If you're new to the poultry-keeping hobby, or an existing enthusiast who wants to expand your flock even though overall space is limited, then buying a few bantams makes a lot of sense. There are plenty to choose from, with most of the popular chicken breeds offering a plentiful supply of bantam versions.

However, it's the so-called 'true

bantams' which, as well as offering all the space-saving benefits of normal 'miniatures', can provide just that little extra dash of interest too.

There is no more than a handful of naturally-occurring, diminutive breeds – that is, none of which has a large fowl counterpart – and one of the most appealing must surely be the Belgian bearded bantam. Nobody can help but be enchanted by these charismatic, proud little birds, which offer no fewer than 12 standardised colour options (and more unofficial variants besides) and three fundamentally different varieties to pick from. Their continued popularity as exhibition birds, as well as with domestic enthusiasts who seek nothing more than a few beautiful birds to keep as pets, ensures that interest in the breed as a whole remains high.

Belgian beginnings

We in the UK weren't introduced to the charms of the Belgian bearded bantam until quite recently, relatively speaking – in 1911, when some fanciers from Belgium staged the first exhibition of their birds at Crystal Palace, in South London. The reception they got was enthusiastic and the breed has hardly looked back since.

On the face of it, things are a little confusing when it comes to classifying the various varieties of this breed. The situation isn't helped by the many colour options, or the tendency for some people to use one of the most popular colour variants – millefleur – as a name in its own right. Fundamentally, though, the two most commonly-found varieties are the exotic-sounding Barbu d'Anvers and the Barbu d'Uccle. 'Barbu' relates to nothing more than the fact that these birds are bearded, while Anvers (Antwerp) and Uccle are simply the Belgian towns of origin.

But telling these two varieties apart is simple, as the differences are pronounced. The d'Anvers has a rose comb and clean legs, while the d'Uccle presents a single comb and feathered legs. There can be no confusion in this respect. There's also a variety called Barbu de Watermael, which is distinguished by its combination of clean legs, beard and head crest. Finally, and perhaps most rare of all, there are rumpless (no tail) versions of both the d'Anvers and the d'Uccle, which are called Barbu du Grubbe and Barbu d'Everberg respectively.

All Belgian bearded bantams are characterised by their small yet proud and bold appearance. They are active little birds with broad and rounded bodies, short legs and backs, and wings that are held

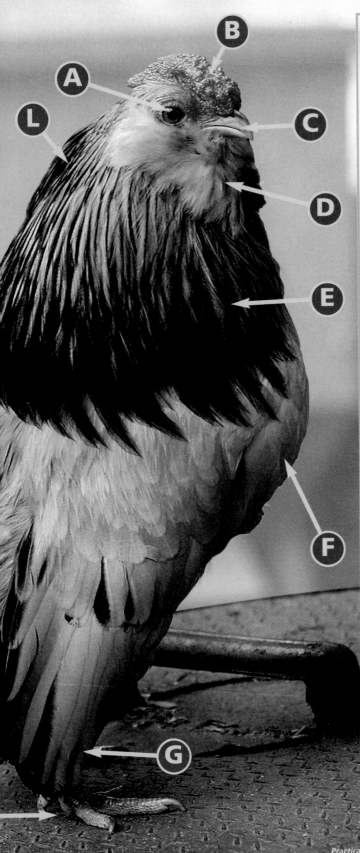

A The eye should be large, bold and as darkly-coloured as possible on a d'Anvers male like this.

B The Barbu d'Anvers should feature a reasonably compact rose comb, with a single, pointed leader running backwards and following the curve of the neck. There should be plenty of workings on the top. The Barbu d'Uccle has a single comb.

C The beak is short and slightly curved. In most varieties it should be horn-coloured, but it will be slate-blue on millefleur, porcelaine and lavender/blue-related colours, and white on the white. Watch out for a twisted beak, which is quite a common problem.

D All these bantams should feature pronounced beard and muff feathers on either side of, and below, the beak. Wattles shouldn't really feature at all. Slight growth may be seen on some male birds, but not on females. It's unwise to breed from females showing any wattle growth; the male offspring will develop significant wattle growth, and the problem will get worse and worse.

E Neck is of moderate length and attractively curved. Both d'Anvers and d'Uccle male birds feature thick, long hackle feather growth, creating a cape effect across the back and shoulders. Female birds have broader hackle feathers.

F Breast should always be broad, prominent and proud.

G Legs should be short with as little thigh as possible. When standing properly, a good male bird's wing tips should all but cover the feet when viewed from the side. If you can see a lot of the foot and lower leg, then the leg is probably too long.

H Barbu d'Anvers have feather-free legs and feet, unlike the d'Uccle. There should be four toes, and the colour of the nails should match the beak.

I Wings are medium length and should be carried at a steep angle like this on male birds, pointing as near to the ground as possible.

J The tail on both d'Anvers and d'Uccle versions features a pair of curved sickle feathers – more sword-shaped on the d'Anvers. On female birds the tail is short, more compact and held at an angle of about 45°.

K Back should be very short, and slanted down towards the base of the tail.

L This area of slightly raised feathers, known as the 'boule', is a characteristic feature of the Belgian bearded bantam.

tight to the body and angled towards the ground. The d'Anvers is perhaps the most characterful, possessing a sort of cockiness that causes it to strut around in an attitude of almost permanent showing-off! The d'Uccle, on the other hand, is slightly more of a relaxed character, and is frequently described as being 'majestic'. Both types show significant neck hackle feather development, and will also feature an area of convexly-shaped feathering on the back of the neck, causing a characteristic mound known as a 'boule'.

The d'Uccle's feathered legs are an important distinguishing factor, and consist of stiff, quill feathers down the outside the legs, and shank feathers on the outside and middle toes. Another more subtle distinction between these two popular varieties concerns the beard and muff feathering. On the d'Uccle this should ideally consist of three distinct, feathery lobes (one under the beak, and others on either side of it). This tends not to be so apparent on the d'Anvers, where this soft feathering forms more of a collar, framing the face.

One other important face-related point is that wattles on this breed should be all but non-existent.

Colour choice

The superb range of colours available with this breed represents one of its major attractions for exhibitors and domestic keepers alike. As far as the rose-combed d'Anvers is concerned, quail is probably the most popular of all. It provides a striking combination of black, buffs and brownse. The black d'Anvers is also very widely kept.

For d'Uccle enthusiasts, two of the most desirable colour options have got to be the spectacular millefleur and porcelaine. These are both variations on a tri-colour theme, with the millefleur showing a golden mahogany ground colour, black spangling and V-shaped white tipping – usually most clearly seen on the breast feathers. In the case of the porcelaine version, the whole colour scheme has been diluted, with the mahogany ground being replaced by a light straw colour, and the black by an attractive pale blue.

However, as far as the serious

Buff mottled d'Uccle hen; one of the many attractive, non-standardised colours

breeder is concerned, colour pales into virtual insignificance in comparison to a bird's type. The way it looks, and its adherence to the breed standard in this respect, is the single most important factor in setting a good bird apart from a bad one. To be successful at a show, a top Belgian bearded bantam must present all the vital characteristics; bold, upright stance, pronounced, arched breast, short back, correct tail, downward-pointing wings and short legs. These aspects can count for anything up to half of the 100 points available to a bird being judged at a show.

Of course, when it comes to buying birds to keep in your back garden, slavishly following the breed standard isn't so important although, as always, the sensible buyer will always source the best birds available at the time. After all, there's no point in knowingly buying substandard examples. All the usual ground rules of purchasing apply – only buy from a recognised supplier (preferably on recommendation); if you're inexperienced, then take someone with you who knows the breed and can help you choose; whenever possible visit the seller, not only to inspect the birds, but also to assess the environment in which they are

being kept; never be afraid to say 'no' and walk away. Remember, buying-in suspect birds will usually cause nothing but trouble!

Practical pointers

Whichever type you eventually decide to buy, it's important to appreciate that the Belgian bearded bantam can be quite a demanding bird to own, particularly if you're interested in showing them. To breed and keep them well requires quite high levels of husbandry. Their size, and closeness to the ground, means that

The d'Uccle's feathered legs can hide parasitic problems such as scaly leg. Keepers need to remain vigilant

An attractively marked Barbu d'Uccle porcelaine female

birds kept in poor conditions can suffer with matted feathers, particularly d'Uccles with their feathered legs.

Having said this, the breed in itself is a reasonably hardy one and, all being well, tends to be robust and long-lived. Despite their diminutive size, these bantams certainly don't demand any special attention over and above the normal basic requirements (good, dry housing, secure enclosure, regular feed and fresh, clean drinking water etc.). There's no need for in-house heating and, of course, they can be happily kept in correspondingly smaller accommodation than would be needed for large fowl.

Another aspect which makes this bantam so popular is its endearing character. They make great garden pets, and won't do too much damage to flower borders or other planted areas. They are 'chatty' too, are perfectly happy being handled and will become extremely tame under the right conditions, but potential owners should be aware of the fact that these birds can be pretty good fliers, so containment can be an issue for those keepers living in urban surroundings.

Some male birds can become a little 'sharp' around breeding time, but this is only to be expected. Generally, though, they aren't outwardly aggressive birds and, even if one does decide to take a peck at your hand, it's not going to do any damage. Having said this, bird-to-bird relationships can be a different matter.

If you intend to start a breeding program with these birds, then bear in mind that the females can be very aggressive towards male birds. To help avoid this it's always a good idea to put the female into the male's pen, rather than the other way around. The hens are quite territorial, so moving a male into a previously female-only pen will probably cause trouble; she won't take kindly to the 'invasion', and is likely to dominate and bully the male. The inevitable consequence of this is that the fertility of the eggs being produced will fall away to nothing.

Careful handling

Still on the subject of eggs, there's another important aspect of ownership to be considered. The hens, while not being prolific layers (about 120 a season), do produce a surprisingly large egg considering their overall size. This means that hens in lay must be handled carefully and gently to avoid damaging the egg (cracking the shell) or rupturing the bird's oviduct. Both of these possibilities pose very serious problems, and will often result in the bird's untimely death.

The risk of damage to the oviduct can also be significantly increased if the birds are overfed, and allowed to become too fat. This is always a potential worry, particularly with birds which are kept as family pets in an environment where space is limited and there is little opportunity for them to get much exercise. There's always a great temptation, especially among children, to feed titbits and treats but, as responsible keepers, we should always guard against this.

Birds which don't have the opportunity to enjoy free-range living conditions will require a carefully controlled diet if problems are to be avoided. The ideal feeding regime should be based around a good quality growers or layers pelleted feed (depending on the age of the birds), lots of straight wheat and plenty of fresh greens. Steer clear of maize as this will promote fattening if used incorrectly.

We've already mentioned that egg fertility can suffer if dominant hens start bullying their mating partners, but don't let this put you off having a go at breeding Belgian bearded bantams. All else being equal, both fertility and hatch rates are very good with these birds. Chick survival rates tend to be high and once they're safely out of the shell they'll go from strength to strength. However, this bantam isn't a recognised broody, so you'll need to hatch your fertile eggs using an incubator, or a seperate broody hen.

Finally, from a general disease resistance point of view, it's good news too! These birds tend not to suffer badly with any of the recognised poultry problems, although random but fatal heart attacks can be the cause of 'out of the blue' deaths. In fact, apart from keeping a close watch on all the usual welfare issues, just about the only thing you need to be particularly mindful of is the presence of parasitic infestation. •

Brahma

Domestic chickens don't come much larger than the
exotic Brahma but, despite this Asiatic giant's size,
it can make a great choice for the novice keeper

A **Beak** should be short and strong and coloured yellow, or yellow and black.

B The Brahma's **comb** is a triple or pea-type, which should be small and close-fitting to the head. It's larger on the male, of course, but still needs to be relatively small and neat.

C It's the **beetle brow** that gives the Brahma its slightly stern look, but it's an important requirement of a good bird, and should be equally prominent on both males and females. The **eye** should be prominent too, and bright orange in colour.

D **Wattles** are small as well, and should balance with the comb on both sexes. Uneven wattle length is a serious fault from an exhibition point of view.

E Brahmas should present a short, flat **back**, that rises slightly towards the base of the tail. Overall body volume is important. Three Brahmas in a sale pen ought to fill it! An adult male should be 24-26in tall. Overall, the bird should present a squarish, cobby appearance; the Shire horse of poultry! The width of a good male bird should be half its overall length, and large show examples these days can weigh up to 16lb – considerably more than the guidelines offered in the breed standard.

F There can be a tendency for elderly females to develop a **Cochin-like cushion tail**, which rather goes against the close-feathering ideals of the Brahma – a much-debated subject over the years.

G Quality of **feather marking** is another important factor. If it's a pencilled bird, like this gold hen, then these markings should be clearly defined and extend from the neck hackle right through to the tail. Blurred or broken-up pencilling is undesirable on females and may point to an inferior breeding line.

H **Wing** should be held tight to the body. Split-wings are a serious fault to avoid. Usually you'll need to spread the wing to check definitely for this, although sometimes it can be visible even when the bird has its wing folded. A useful indicator can be the resistance you feel as you actually spread the wing. If it feels slack then the chances are that there's a weakness in the feathering.

I **Legs** should be moderately long, well-spaced, powerful and yellow. Avoid white legs. Lower breast feathers should cover part-way down the front of the legs, fluff should be abundant and extend back behind the thighs. The lower leg should be well-feathered too, as should the middle and outer toes.

J **Foot feathering** on the best examples can extend out as much as 6in/125mm to the side.

K **Breast** should be full and rounded. Avoid birds showing a cutaway breast.

There can be few breeds offering quite the sense of presence as the Brahma. If you like your chickens large and impressive, then this really is the breed for you! These birds are tall, wide and extremely well-feathered. Large bodies stand on strong, widely-spaced and feathered legs; the Brahma truly is an Asiatic giant.

Although widely listed as a breed from Asia, the general consensus now is that the Brahma was actually created in America, during the 1840s. However, there's plenty of disagreement surrounding the precise way in which this happened, although it seems likely that imported stock from India (the Grey Chittagong) and China (the Shanghai) were used in the crossing mix. Whether or not the Cochin was involved as well remains unclear.

Royal boost

The new breed really came to prominence when the first examples arrived in England during 1852; they'd been sent as a present for Queen Victoria from a publicity-seeking American breeder called George Burnham. He supplied nine birds – described then as Grey Shanghais – and, soon after they arrived, renowned poultry artist Harrison Weir was commissioned by the *Illustrated London News* to record the exotic-looking fowl.

The name 'Brahma' was derived from an abbreviation of 'Brahmaputra'; one of the great Asian rivers, which flows from China, through India and Bangladesh, and out into the Bay of Bengal. The first birds were apparently dispatched to America from a port at the mouth of this river, so it was thought appropriate that the resultant breed should take its name from the region of its roots.

Queen Victoria's Grey Shanghais were from the strain that was ultimately to become the Light Brahma. It was this and the Dark version that provided the mainstay of the breed initially, but nowadays there's a little more choice. The standardised colours available today are the dark, the light, the white, the gold, the buff Columbian and, newest of all, the blue partridge.

The arrival of the 'eBay era' has introduced the world to a wide variety of cross-breeds in assorted, non-standard colours, including blue pyle, blue and black. While it's claimed by breeders that some of these new versions breed reliably, it should be noted that many certainly don't. There's an even greater colour variety available on the Continent, especially in Holland.

A slipped wing can be a problem with Brahmas. Look for a gap in the flight featherslike this when spreading the wing

But whichever standardised colour you choose, a well-bred Brahma will prove to be a striking bird that manages to be both sedate and active at the same time. It is broad, square and deep, with a short back and profuse but relatively tight feathering together with large, widely-spaced, strong feathered-legs. A small head and short beak seem to accentuate the impression of overall size and, coupled with large eyes, heavy beetle brows and a small, pea-type comb, create a distinctive, somewhat grumpy look!

However, it's the Brahma's docile personality that many keepers find so enchanting; a factor that belies the outwardly burly appearance. These birds are among the gentlest you'll find, and the males don't have an 'angry bone' in their bodies. As a result the breed is ideally suited to the back garden environment and family situations.

Size does matter

Bantam versions are available, but don't seem to represent a particularly popular ownership option, especially in club circles. Perhaps part of the problem is that the Brahma is famous for being a large, rustic type of bird, so keeping a miniature version rather defeats the object. Also, from an exhibition point of view, the old adage about a good big 'un always beating a good little 'un seems to apply.

With regard to actually buying large fowl Brahmas, the situation is relatively good. But don't forget

A good male head, showing compact comb, orange eye, clean face and even wattles

that, as seems to be the case with so many pure breeds these days, the number of serious, experienced breeders is decreasing all the time. It's been suggested that, currently, there are fewer than ten experts producing top-quality stock in the UK, despite the fact that the Brahma Club is enjoying a buoyant

period and boasts 100+ members. It may be the case that most of the members simply keep the birds because they love them, and have no real interest in either breeding or showing.

Traditionally, the attractive lights and darks have been the most popular colour options, although

You can get a good idea of the relative size of Brahmas by comparing these two gold hens with the not insubstantial hybrid layers beside them

Brahma at a glance

Plus points: Impressive size, docile nature, great family bird, hardy, easy to breed

Minus points: Prone to leg mite, labour-intensive to show, getting harder to find

Size: Heavy, soft feather

Origin: India/America

Weights:
Male – 4.55-5.45kg (10-12lbs)
Female – 3.20-4.10kg (7-9lbs)
Bantam male – 1,080g (38oz) max
Bantam female – 910g (32oz) max

Egg laying: 100+ pa

Colours: dark, light, white, gold, buff Columbian, blue partridge

the gold is becoming a very popular show bird nowadays. Somewhat surprisingly, the pretty buff Columbian appears to be a singularly unsuccessful show bird, with some suggesting that it tends to present too much fluffiness for most judges' tastes. However, the cost of birds isn't really influenced by their colour and, as a guide, you should expect to pay £25-40 per bird for good, large fowl examples.

The Brahma is a slow-maturing bird, so in their first year they never look that special (half-grown teenagers!). This is something to bear in mind when buying young stock. Brahmas won't assume their full magnificence until they reach maturity, during the second year. But keepers need have no fear about these birds being weak and vulnerable during the growing stages. The Brahma is a tough and hardy breed. It is active and loves nothing better than a free-range lifestyle, although this isn't ideal if you intend showing. An outdoor existence will play merry hell with the foot feathering, so serious exhibitors tend to keep their best examples in covered runs.

Thankfully, the Brahma's placid nature means that confinement doesn't create problems, assuming the birds are given an amount of space that reflects their large size.

Brahmas are all about width, and even females like this gold can cut an impressive dash in this respect!

While top fanciers have been known to keep single birds in 6x4' enclosures, a trio of birds kept at a domestic level should be perfectly happy in a 4x4' enclosure, provided they have access to a garden too.

The Brahma isn't a flier; hopping is about as good as it gets for these large birds! As a result, retaining fences need only be 4ft/1.2m high

within a secured area, and it's unlikely that you'll ever have to worry about these birds going AWOL. This aspect, together with their docility of character, means that Brahmas are very easy birds to own, even for a novice keeper. Handling isn't a problem (assuming you're strong enough to lift them!), and both males and females will be extremely tolerant of handling by children.

Practical aspects
The general ease of ownership associated with the Brahma means that there are few problems to worry about for keepers new to the breed. These birds aren't characteristically prone to any of the common poultry ailments, which leaves feather-related parasite issues as the only real area for concern.

As with any feathered-leg breed, Brahmas tend to be more prone to scaly leg mite than clean-legged birds, and this is a condition that owners need to be particularly aware of. Regular checks will be required, and effective measures taken swiftly if any tell-tale scale-lifting is spotted. Lice and mites

Watch for white feathering where it shouldn't be. You're most likely to spot it in the wings, across all colour varieties

elsewhere on the body can be an issue too, so frequent dusting and top-notch poultry house maintenance are essential as part of your good husbandry routine.

Brahmas tend to be easy birds to breed, typically showing good levels of fertility and hatch rates. Results are often best when hatching occurs early in the year (January/February), and the chicks are usually strong growers; if they get out of the shell OK you can usually rest assured that they'll be fine.

Undercolour is another important issue, in terms of overall quality. As a general rule, the darker the grey on golds and darks, the better. It's obviously lighter on the lights. Buff Columbians can have a tendency towards a white undercolour, which is unwelcome if intending to show. Light undercolour can be the forerunner of white feathering where it shouldn't be

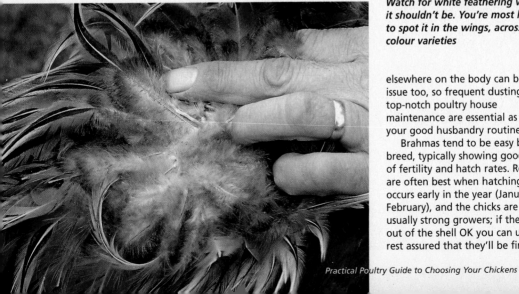

Just about the only condition to watch for among newly-hatched chicks is splayed legs – sometimes they're just too big for their own good. Experienced keepers are able to sex chicks at a very early age, based on subtle differences in head shape. Those without such expertise, however, should be able to tell male from female by the six-week mark, using tail angle as a guide. On male birds it'll be vertical and short, while a female's tail is held horizontally, and will be noticeably longer by that age.

Brahma hens make great broodies, but the large fowl can be a little clumsy (bantams are obviously better); weight and the foot feathering are the key issues in this respect. A good compromise can be to hatch using an incubator and then give the day-old chicks to a broody hen to rear as her own. Other keepers take advantage of the broodiness by using Brahma hens to hatch thicker-shelled duck and goose eggs.

Weight control

The hens will lay relatively well for a pure breed, although the selective breeding that's gone on to boost size and feathering for exhibition purposes has hindered this utility aspect. Another key influence on a hen's laying ability is body weight. Brahmas have tremendous appetites, so running to fat is always a background risk if the birds are given too much food. This is another very good reason for allowing the birds to free-range – the exercise will help keep the weight in check.

Big hens reared for the show pen tend to lay very few eggs once they get to two or three years old. Young, healthy pullets are perfectly capable of laying 100 eggs in a season. But if you're main objective is egg production, then the Brahma probably isn't you're best bet. When you compare the amount of food that goes in one end, versus the number of eggs produced from the other, the result doesn't make a

Vulture hocks have long been an undesirable feature on the Brahma, but many birds still have them. The trouble is that trying to breed to replace these stiff, downward-facing feathers with softer, more acceptable alternatives tends to cause a reduction in foot and leg feathering, which is a much more serious exhibition-related fault

lot of economic sense. So overfeeding is certainly something to be avoided, especially if the birds are being kept in confinement. The most common consequence of excessive weight in males is a fatal heart attack, typically as they attempt to treat a female. Watch for discolouration of the headgear following exertion; if it 'purples' after the bird's been running, or when it's picked up, then there's most likely a weight problem. Hens suffering in the same way will become progressively more lethargic; they'll stop running to greet you and will simply plod around the place.

The friendliness of a healthy Brahma is perhaps one of its most endearing characteristics. These birds reward their owners not only with spectacular, majestic looks but also with a level of companionship in the garden which takes some beating. The breed really does represent a cracking choice for the beginner, and while Brahma keepers definitely will not find these birds particularly cheap to keep due to their large appetites, if you've got some spare ground on which you can let a few of these majestic fowl free-range, they'll be perfectly happy to supplement their diet from what's freely available in mother nature's larder! •

Some have likened the Brahma's profile to that of a wine glass, and this gold male illustrates why

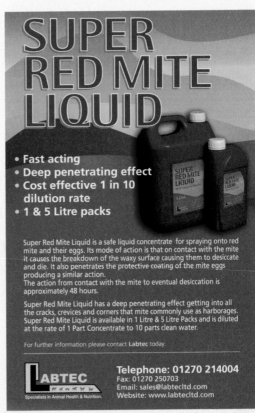

Cochin

If you're looking for a large and friendly chicken that'll be kind to your children as well as your garden, then the Cochin could be the ideal breed

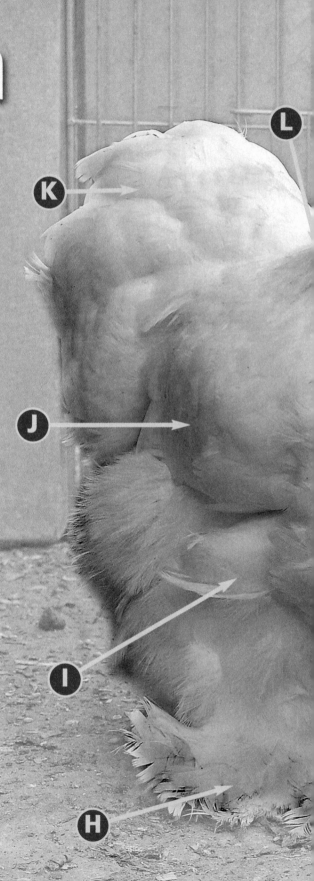

The exotic-sounding Cochin is a very significant breed as far as the poultry-keeping hobby is concerned. Not only does it present many great qualities for the world-be domestic owner, but the bird is widely credited as the one which inspired a nation to begin regarding chickens as creatures of beauty and desirability, rather than simply functional livestock.

It was the Cochin's royal connections which really set the ball rolling; Queen Victoria proved a very influential and trend-setting owner during the mid-1800s. It was her early patronage which transformed the Cochin into a fashionable 'must-have' bird among the aristocracy and landed gentry. The craze spread to the middle classes too, and it wasn't long before people began showing their birds. So the poultry exhibition scene was born.

The other consequence of the Cochin's rapid rise in popularity was that demand for it heightened, and the value of the best examples sky-rocketed to levels fanciers can only dream of today. However, it's important to appreciate that the Cochin of the mid-1850s was a very different creature from the bird we have today. Originally brought into this country as an exotic breed with useful utility qualities – a good layer and tasty table bird – the originals were taller, rangier and with a lot less foot feathering and 'fluffiness' than we see today.

It was those in the poultry 'fancy' who initiated this change. Successive generations of showmen, breeding carefully and specifically for the show pen, created the breed's 'feather duster' appearance simply because they liked the look of it. Unfortunately, the price paid for such visual indulgence was that laying performance was lost – chickens can't produce both eggs and feathers.

Currently there are six standardised plumage colours recognised by the Poultry Club of Great Britain: Buff, Blue, Black, White, Cuckoo and Partridge. There are other versions around too,

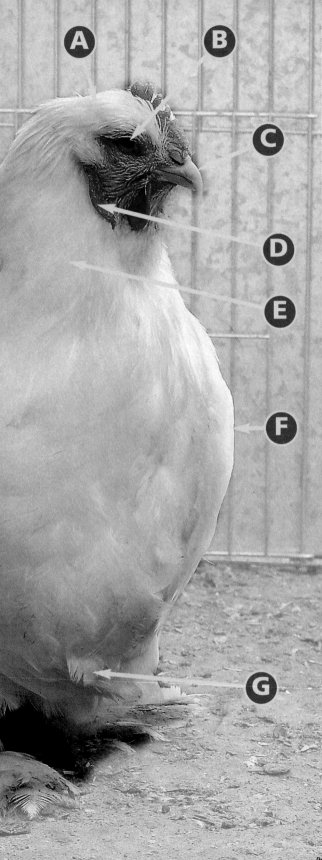

A A Cochin's head should be small and evenly shaped. There should be no sign of a 'beetle brow' and the comb should be single and small, especially on female birds, like this one (a Cochin Club champion).

B The eye should be bold and bright and either coloured deep red or hazel/dark in the Black versions.

C The beak should be short, curved and stout at its base. The colour can be either yellow, horn or black.

D A feature of the Cochin is its long, bright red ear lobes, which are very pronounced on the male. The wattles, however, tend to be small in both sexes, but equally red. If they are uneven, that's a fault.

E The neck is on the short side and curved. The really important thing is that it's profusely covered with flowing hackle feathers – more so on the male.

F The breast should be deep, wide and profusely feathered.

G In some exhibition hens the feathering on the breast can be so great that it almost touches the ground at the front.

H Feet should be very well feathered, particularly on the middle and outside toes. Ideally, the inner toe should be feathered too, but finding this is rare. Make sure that the bird has four toe nails on each foot. Some strains have been selected for the absence of these, which is a serious fault. They can also be lost due to poor husbandry. Feet need to be regularly inspected to check for mats of muck which, if allowed to build-up, can promote problems.

I While the Cochin's plumage may seem a little daunting, don't let it put you off. With good husbandry and common sense it's perfectly possible to keep these birds in tip-top condition. All those included here were lifted straight from their pens and photographed in their 'everyday' clothes.

J The body must feature extremely broad and pronounced shoulders, especially on the female. Wings must be short and well tucked into the sides of the body, and barely visible to the casual observer. Thighs need to be large and profusely feathered. Overall the bird should have a 'lumpy' appearance created by billowing mounds of soft feather.

K The tail mustn't show any of the traditional, distinctive and stiff feathers as found on other breeds, even on the male bird. The male also shouldn't show much of a tail rise above the level of the back. On the female the tail should be virtually hidden by the softly-rounded cushion.

L The back should be broad yet very short, leading into the 'cushion' that should be very pronounced on the female.

HISTORY

- The Cochin is widely regarded as the original 'aristocratic' fowl.
- First imported into the UK by merchant seamen during the mid-1800s, allegedly from Shanghai.
- Initially known as 'Shanghais', then name switched to 'Cochin Chinas' before being shortened to 'Cochin'.
- Origins not absolutely clear; there's still a port on the west coast of India called Cochin.
- The first birds were presented to Queen Victoria in the early 1840s, which eventually sparked a nationwide interest in exhibiting and poultry keeping.
- Initial popularity of the breed meant that values soared. In the 1870s good Partridge Cochins were selling for over 100 guineas each.
- The record price paid for a bird, seen at one of the poultry shows in Birmingham around 1880, was over £300 – an absolute fortune in those days!

including Frizzle, Buff Columbian and Blue Columbian, but these aren't recognised by the Poultry Club here or the Cochin Club.

Sourcing Cochins

The breed has retained its stately appearance, and still holds a good deal of appeal for all sorts of domestic keepers. However, buying good ones is perhaps not as

Partridge male. Note large ear lobes, even black breast and good thigh fluff

Of this group of White Cochin youngsters, the two on the left with their tails towards the camera, and the one in the foreground on the right (looking away), would be the ones not to buy. They are showing poor shoulder width, and poor type generally

the Cochin has an abundance of fluff on this upper part of the leg.

The popularity of the various plumage colours seems to vary from year to year. This season the Blue has been in high demand whereas, last year it was the Buff which everyone was after. It's largely a matter of personal preference, but it's worth noting that the Partridge is perhaps the scarcest of all.

Feather issues

The profuse foot and leg feathering means that Cochins can have an increased tendency to be sufferers with scaly-leg mite, Northern mite and lice. Owners need to be extra vigilant with regular, careful inspections and a preventative programme against these parasites is certainly advisable. What's more, be careful not to allow the birds exposure to coal dust, as this will irritate the scales on the leg, allowing the mites easier access.

Feathered feet can cause a problem for laying hens. They are quite cumbersome and awkward when it comes to manoeuvring in the nest box. The risk is that eggs may get cracked (particularly if you're slow to collect them) which, in turn, can promote very undesirable egg-eating. For this reason, some keepers clip the foot feathers to eliminate this risk. Others also find that the abundant feathering around the vent can interfere with breeding, and so these are clipped back too.

Shoulder width is all-important in Cochin females. A straight, single comb is something else to look for

straightforward as it is with some of the other, more numerous, pure breeds. As always, we'd recommend that anyone interested in buying should first of all seek advice from The Cochin Club. While there are currently fewer than 100 members, they are spread pretty well across the UK, so there should be a useful and reliable source of good quality stock within striking distance for most people.

Unfortunately, the relative scarcity of Cochins has fostered a market for 'lookalikes', which are unscrupulously sold as the genuine article. Typically, breeders cross Cochins with Brahmas to produce weird and wonderful offspring which they then try to pass-off as pure-bred Cochins. But the Brahma has a shallower head than the Cochin, and a triple comb that's obviously different from the Cochin's single one. Brahmas are noticeably taller too, and feature vulture hocks – stiff, angled feathers on the hock. In contrast,

With Black Cochins, it's permissible to have yellow, horn or black beaks, and red, hazel or almost black eyes

Wings should always be checked carefully for twisted feathers and 'split wing' (the presence of an obvious step between the primary and secondary feathers)

These young females are exactly the same age, but the one on the right is showing much better shoulder width, and would be the one to buy

Practical pointers

There are two key issues to bear in mind if you're thinking about buying Cochins. The first concerns the breed's foot feathering, which can pose some potentially serious practical problems if good husbandry standards aren't maintained.

The most basic requirement is that this feathering is kept dry. Dampness poses a real threat to these birds, which is why many experienced keepers have their stock indoors during wet periods. They should certainly be contained during the winter months, and at other times when the weather is damp. Houses and covered runs should have a good, deep layer of

Ideal female 'cushion'; gently rounded and incorporating the tail completely

clean, fresh and dry straw or softwood shavings.

Birds allowed to get wet can stay like this for a long while because of their profuse feathering. If allowed to continue, this will cause a significant drain on the constitution, and can promote stress. As we all know, stress is a potentially dangerous condition for any chicken, because it works to lower the bird's resistance to all sorts of disease and infection. Consequently, stressed birds are far more prone to health problems than those which are happy and contented.

The other big factor to bear in mind is that the Cochin is a very docile breed and, despite its size, it will tend to get bullied if run in a mixed flock. The only way it can be safe to mix them is if all the birds have been reared together. Trying to introduced adult Cochins into an established group of other birds simply won't work. To be on the safe side, Cochins are best kept in isolation.

Their calm disposition means they'll tolerate confinement well, assuming they're not overcrowded. But they love being out on grass too (short and dry is best), and will certainly benefit from some gentle free-ranging during the summer.

The Cochin is a good breed to have around the garden; its essentially lazy nature means that plant damage will be minimal, and individual birds won't roam far either. They're not classified as fliers, so fencing of just a few feet high should be quite sufficient for keeping them contained. Obviously, though, this will be no good for keeping predators out, which is an important point because the Cochin certainly isn't a 'streetwise' breed; they will stand and watch a fox!

Many owners love the Cochin for its great 'family qualities' – the breed is good with children, thrives on companionship and becomes very attached to its owners given time. There's also no problem with handling; the birds love it! However, on the downside it's worth noting that the male birds aren't quiet. They produce a characteristically long crow which could well pose problems for would-be keepers living in urban environments.

Cochin hens make good broody mums but, as already mentioned, laying performance certainly isn't what it once was. The eggs produced are smaller than you might expect – considering the size of the bird – and a good hen will lay no more than 150 a season. Pullets will lay well in the winter, but not when compared to other out-and-out utility breeds like the Light Sussex or Leghorn.

From an exhibition point of view, Cochins definitely improve with age. So it can be that when a hen reaches her show best, she might be five or six years old, and could well have stopped laying altogether.

YES OR NO?

✔ Good family bird.
✔ Placid, friendly nature.
✔ Easily handled.
✔ Stately, 'aristocratic' appearance.
✔ Non-fliers and 'garden-friendly'.
✔ Happy in confinement.
✔ Good table bird.

✘ Very moisture-sensitive.
✘ Don't mix well.
✘ Not a great layer.
✘ Males are noisy crowers.
✘ Parasite problems.
✘ No bantam version in UK.

Croad Langshan

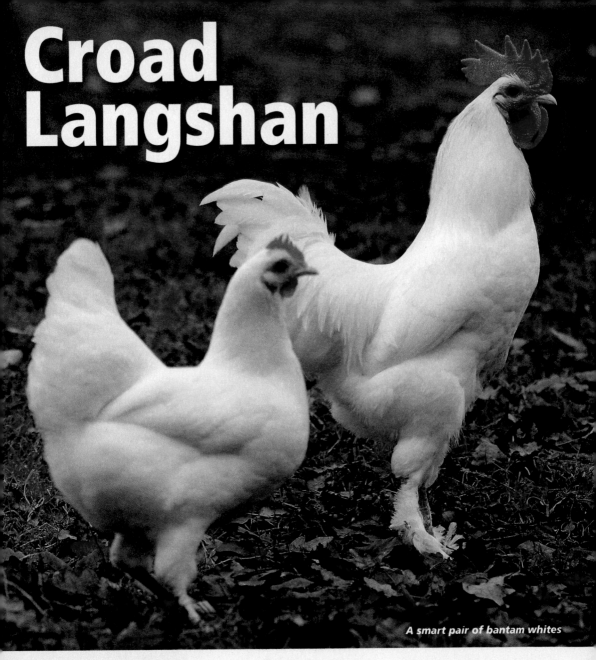

A smart pair of bantam whites

An interesting Asiatic breed with all the utility performance you could reasonably hope for

The Croad Langshan, the original type brought to the UK by Major F T Croad in 1872, caused something of a stir following its first public appearance at London's Crystal Palace that year.

The breed, which Croad had imported from the Langshan region of northern China, was immediately compared with the Cochin. In fact, many people started claiming that the two breeds were one and the same thing. The idea wouldn't go away and although today any apparent confusion between the two breeds might seem hard to fathom, things were far less clear 135 years ago.

The Cochin we know today – a breed developed exclusively for its impressive softness and profusion of feathering – is a far cry from the type of bird that was imported from China all those years ago. Towards the end of the 19th century, the Cochin and the Langshan may well have looked quite similar, hence the dispute. But

Black large fowl male displaying sleek plumage with plenty of the all-important beetle-green sheen in evidence

Croad stuck to his guns, maintaining the Langshan's separate roots.

However, the distinction wasn't clear enough for those fanciers who, when exhibiting their birds, became fed up having to deal with all the confusion. Consequently, a breakaway group began adjusting the breed's appearance, principally by increasing leg length, to create what became known as the Modern Langshan. These are now very rare in the UK, with only two examples on show at the recent Federation Show in Stafford.

Useful utility

Croad remained resolute, continuing to breed for the Langshan's best utility qualities. The breed we have available to us now must surely rank as one of the most suitable for today's domestic poultry enthusiast. At some point along the way, the breed took the Major's name, although the story has it that he named the bird after his niece, in recognition of the effort she put into supporting the breed.

The Croad Club was established in 1904 and, the breed's impressive utility qualities really came to the fore during the hard, inter-war years, when the birds also performed well in laying trials. This popularity dwindled soon after the Second World War, presumably in the face of the competition from the American-

AT A GLANCE

Size
Large fowl; heavy, soft feather.
Bantam

Weights
Large male - 4.10kg (9lbs)
Bantam male - 770-910g
                    (27-32oz)
Large female – 3.20kg (7lb)
Bantam female – 650-790g
                    (23-28oz)

Egg laying
180+ pa

Colours
Black, white

A The beak should be a light to dark horn colour, and tends to be darker on the black birds, preferably with light at the tip and streaked with grey. Overall, the beak should be of average size and slightly curved.

B The comb must always be red, single, upright and never too large. Ideally, a show judge will expect to see five spikes, but more than this is common. Face should be a matching red, and free from feathers.

C Eye should be dark, not orange or red. The standard calls for Van Dyke brown, or the colour of a ripe hazelnut. Avoid birds with light coloured eyes.

D Wattles should not be too large and coloured to match comb and face. Watch out for white in the lobes as this is a serious fault to be avoided.

E Distinct U-shape created by the neck, back and tail is a Croad Langshan characteristic. Head should sit at the same height as the top of the tail when the bird is active and alert.

F Male tail should feature a couple of sweeping sickle feathers that arc noticeably higher than the main body of the tail.

G A good male Croad will show plenty of side hanger feathers on either side of the tail. The saddle hackle feathering should effectively smooth out the join between the back and the base of the tail.

H These birds aren't great fliers. Smallish wings are held high and tight against the sides of the body, which is wide at the shoulder.

I Avoid too much feathering on the legs. What there is should simply run down the outside edge of the leg and outer toe.

J Legs should be clean on the inside, with a bluish/ black skin colour (generally lighter on the white variety). They should neither be too long or too short, so that the bird remains in graceful proportion overall.

K Breast needs to be well-rounded and deep. Neck well covered with hackle feathers on the male, and of medium length with a graceful curve.

This red pigmentation down the outside of a mature male bird's leg is perfectly acceptable

developed hybrids that were instrumental in the demise of so many of the pure-bred layers. Thankfully, the Croad Langshan was saved by the sterling efforts of the Rare Poultry Society and then, in 1979, the club was reformed so the breed had independence once again.

There's no doubt that the Croad Langshan offers many advantages and one of the most appealing must be its wonderful combination of graceful alertness and straightforward good looks. It's quite rare for a breed of this size to have retained such elegance and this, in itself, sets it apart from many others. The breed's shortish back, deep, rounded keel and upright stance give it a stately, elegant presence that's hard to beat. Yet the Croad Langshan is certainly much more than just a good looker. At a practical level, it offers its keepers just about everything that could be wished for.

Limited choice

The Croad Langshan is only available in two standardised plumage colours. Black was the original, and a white was developed from this (using sports). Both colours are pure, but it's essential that the blacks show a prominent, beetle-green sheen to their feathers. A number of enthusiasts have blue bantams at various stages of development but blue isn't an approved colour as yet and, for the time being, the Club doesn't recognise it.

Bantam versions of both the standardised colours are also available, and it's probably true to

say that the bantams are more popular as a show bird, while the large fowl enjoy a strong following among backyard keepers.

The good news, for those of you already interested in keeping Croads, is that because it remains a relatively rare breed, the quality of the stock available tends to be pretty good, assuming you buy from a recognised supplier, of course! As with virtually any other breed, you can find poor examples of Croad Langshans going under the hammer in local livestock sales and auctions. But if you direct you enquiries through the breed club and choose to get your birds from an established and experienced breeder, then the chances are that you'll secure some good stock.

This breed is all about 'type'. It's got to look right. Although big birds (adult, large males can weigh 10+lbs), a good Croad should never look heavy or clumsy. While standing tall, the male birds should be broad across the shoulder and breast, and appear shorter-backed than the female. Ideally, you want to see a U-shape created between the neck, back and tail, but this is often less pronounced on hens. The breast should be deep and rounded, the wings held high and close and the tail held upright. With the bird standing upright and alert, the top of the head should match the height of the tail. The male tail should feature plenty of saddle hackle and side hanger feathers, plus a couple of pronounced sickles that arch up appreciably higher than the main tail feathers.

The Croad Langshan is a bird of curves, with breeders talking of a 'wine glass' effect that can be seen in the best examples. When viewed from the side, the breed's longish, moderately feathered legs draw the eye up to the 'body' of the glass, with curves created by rounded breast and abdomen, and a similarly-proportioned curving shape produced between neck, back and tail.

Other benefits

The good news doesn't end with this breed's good looks. The Croad's utility credentials make for impressive reading too. Healthy young hens should be capable of

Croad Langshan feet need to be pink on the underside

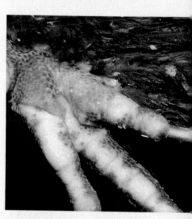

The underside of this foot isn't as pink as it should be, and also features some dark mottling. Not a good sign

Watch out for 'rogue' feathers – black in whites, and white in blacks. But the odd white foot feather in a black is characteristic

The Croad is a keen forager

kept. Make sure that the former aren't too small, and that the latter not too high. Heavy birds can injure their legs and feet if forced to jump down off roosting perches that are set too high.

Another consequence of the breed's innate ruggedness is that fertility levels are usually good. The male birds perform well and the eggs produced enjoy high hatch rates, whether you're dealing with large fowl or bantams. The hens make very attentive mothers too, and their size means that a large hen will happily (and reliably) incubate 10–12 eggs without a problem.

Good Croad Langshan eggs show a very attractive pinkish bloom on the shell, which is most desirable. It can be washed off to reveal the mid-brown shell colour beneath

laying 180 good-sized eggs a year (impressive for a traditional pure-breed), with reasonably dark brown shells and an attractive pinky/plum-coloured bloom. What's more, production will continue well into the winter months. The bantams lay similarly well, although the eggs are correspondingly smaller.

Hardiness is another key factor in the Croad's favour. These birds will happily endure the most exposed of moorland hillside, and are content to forage in all weathers. Free-ranging is the lifestyle they prefer but, if confinement is necessary, they will tolerate this too. As long as the house/ run conditions are good, and there's no overcrowding, then life in a restricted area shouldn't pose a problem.

Being classified as a 'heavy' breed means that the Croad Langshan is a poor flier so, assuming moderate run fencing (five-foot should be fine), you won't find the birds straying into everyone else's gardens. These birds are quiet and docile too, so the annoyance potential for any neighbours should be kept to a minimum.

The fact that these birds have calm and friendly characters means that they are absolutely great in the domestic environment. They make a wonderful family bird that, given good welfare and husbandry levels, will be easy and rewarding to tame. Aggressive examples are extremely rare, and are generally confined to the bantams; but 'sparky' individuals really are unusual.

At a practical level, the Croad Langshan's high degree of hardiness ensures that it's a straightforward breed to keep. It's not known as a specific sufferer with any of the common poultry complaints, and it demands no special favours. However, inexperienced keepers would do well to check pop holes and house perches if large fowl are being

So there you have it. The Croad Langshan really is a breed worth serious consideration if you're seeking a practical, hardy, good-looking and genuinely useful bird. Their docility means that any sort of trouble is very rare (they can get picked on in mixed flocks by more forceful breeds), and they are ideal birds to keep around children. Egg production is impressive and, if you're inclined to try it, their meat is extremely tasty too. It really is hard to imagine anyone wanting more from a chicken. •

YES OR NO?

- ✔ **Calm.**
- ✔ **Great family bird.**
- ✔ **Hardy.**
- ✔ **Plenty of brown eggs.**
- ✔ **Easy to keep.**

✘ **Nothing significant!**

Dorking

B

C

D

A

E

H

F

G

L

The famous, five-toed fowl from the Home Counties which, despite it's quintessentially British image, can be traced back to Italy!

J

K

There can be few poultry breeds packing such an historical punch as the Dorking. This practical, British utility bird simply knocks the opposition into the weeds when it comes to its documented past. Forget 100 years old... forget 200 years old... this breed can be traced back some 2,000 years, to the time of the Roman conquest of Britain!

Of course, precise details of the breed's early development are lost in the murky past, but it does seem likely that the Romans – who we know were partial to eating chicken – brought a large, square-framed, short-legged and five-toed fowl with them. Nowadays the Dorking is available in five distinct plumage colours, but the version introduced by the Romans was probably the forerunner of what we know today as the Red.

It took a long while before some concerted crossing with Sussex and Surrey fowl set in train the development of the 'modern day' Dorking family, which now consists of the rose-combed White, the Dark (formerly called

A A Dorking's headgear should all be bright red. The face should be smooth, and the ear lobes should hang down to about one third of the length of the large wattles. Anything other than a bright red lobe indicates a crossbred bird.

B Watch out for crooked or crossed beak, and check that the nostrils are clear and dry. Remember that Dorkings can be prone to respiratory problems, so avoid birds with 'running noses' or those which are sneezing or gurgling. Put your ear to the side of the bird's body to check that its breathing is quiet.

C There are important comb differences between the colours (see 'At A Glance' box-out, page 45). Single combs, as on this Dark male, should be upright, reasonably large, broad at the base and evenly serrated. Avoid those with side sprigs.

D Eye colour must be a bright red/orange across all plumage colours. A pale eye, or a brown one, is wrong. Pale red/orange, however, may just be showing simply because the bird is young.

E Dark Dorkings should have dark grey ear tufts like this. On the Silver Grey, these will be white; an obvious recognition point.

F Neck hackle feathers on the Dark Dorking should show obvious striping like this, but are plain, silvery-white on the Silver Grey.

G Good length of back is important. Too short is a problem, and can indicate that the bird has been crossed with something else. Birds should feel substantial when handled, not simply a ball of fluff.

H A little white in the primary sickle feathers in a Dark's tail is permissible, but white in the side hangers (seen here at the base of the tail) is not desirable from an exhibition point of view.

I Dorking tails should be full and sweeping, with broad, well-curved sickle feathers. Watch for – and avoid – birds with wry or squirrel tails. These conditions can point to a deformity with the back, which is another serious exhibition fault.

J Legs must be pure or pinky-white. Any duskiness or yellow is a sign of crossbreeding. Avoid 'leggy' birds and look for 'fine', strong bones, not big and coarse. Leg bones should be rounded, not 'squared'. Check the position of the leg spur on male birds. They should be growing inwards on the inside of the leg, but sometimes you'll find them doing the opposite.

K Straight toes are important. Crooked ones can result from a hatching problem, but can also be hereditary, so it's best not to take the risk in the first place if you're intending to breed. Also make sure that all the toes have nails. Sometimes these can be missing (an inherited problem) and while this isn't a desperate problem for the bird, an exhibition judge will spot the defect immediately. Darks are allowed horn-coloured toenails (matching the beak), while all the others should have light nails matching the legs.

L Make sure the breast bone is straight. Crookedness my have been caused by perching problems when the bird was young, or it may be something more fundamental. Silver Grey, Dark and Red must have pure black breast feathering – no white feathers at all. A slight greyish mottling is acceptable on older birds.

The single combs on male Dorkings must be upright. Avoid examples like this Silver Grey with it falling to one side

Despite being a large, heavy and relatively hardy breed, the Dorking is quite sensitive to environmental conditions. Damp, draughty and dirty housing is a real no-no; it'll promote all sorts of respiratory problems. This is a hen, so the falling comb on this Silver Grey is perfectly acceptable

'Coloured'), the Red, the Silver Grey and the Cuckoo. In terms of overall purity it's either the White or the Red that holds the crown, depending on which reference book you read. However, both are rarities now, and it's the Silver Grey which has assumed the mantle of most popular Dorking.

Victorian fancy

The Dorking became a popular exhibition breed among Victorian fanciers, with the Silver Grey proving a particular favourite. But it was the breed's success as a meat bird that really put it on the map. The White was most desirable in this respect, with customers in London associating its pure white flesh and skin with good breeding and refinement.

Some of the key points which made the Dorking such a good meat bird have remained as desirable features right to the present day. Exhibitors strive to produce birds with a straight, flat back that, at a practical level, ensures the bird will

sit well on the plate. Also, another important requirement of exhibition stock is that they should present a deep and well rounded breast, with a long, straight keel bone. These characteristics, of course, mean that it's then possible to carve attractively long slices of breast meat.

All five plumage colours survive today – although some only just. It's thanks to the sterling efforts of the enthusiastic breeders within the Dorking Club that a full choice remains. The White and Cuckoo have struggled for survival in recent times, but are being determinedly nurtured now. In the case of the Cuckoo, this has required some out-crossing which means that type has suffered, but this project is very much a 'work in progress'. The Dark went through a similar popularity dip a few years ago, but was successfully pulled back from the brink by the club.

Bantams do now exist in all colours, but these have had a chequered past too. Unlike most other breeds, bantam versions of

Silvery-white hackle feathers and ear tuft characterise the Silver Grey Dorking; still the most popular colour. The Dorking head should be large and stately but, at the same time, fine

Five toes are obviously essential, but take time to check for Bumblefoot-like swellings on the soles of the feet – birds which regularly perch too high can suffer with this painful condition. Curing bad cases can be difficult. Toe nails should be kept short at all times as this can induce twisted toes if the birds are not able to free range and keep them short by scratching. Legs must be completely featherless

AT A GLANCE

Size
Large; heavy soft feather

Origin
England

Weights
Large male – 4.55-6.35kg (10-14lb)
Large female – 3.60-4.55kg (8-10lb)
Bantam male – 1,130-1,360g (40-48oz)
Bantam female – 910-1,130g (32-40oz)

Egg laying
150+ pa

Colours
Silver Grey, Dark, Red, White and Cuckoo

Comb types

Silver-grey	Single
Dark	Single or Rose
Red	Single
White	Rose
Cuckoo	Rose

the Dorking have never really caught on; most keepers seeming to prefer concentrating on the utility aspects of the large fowl. Part of the problem may also have been that a lot of out-crossing went on in the past, with breeds such as Old English Game and Dutch bantams being added to the mix. As you might imagine, this had a very detrimental effect on the Dorking type and it's been a hard slog pulling type back into line but, once again, the club has come to the rescue. Overall, though, numbers remain limited at present.

Everyone should aim to source the best stock they possibly can, and this means buying your birds through the breed club. But it's also important to appreciate that Dorkings simply aren't bred by the hundred nowadays. It's unlikely that you'll find a breeder with countless examples to choose from – you may have to place an order months ahead of delivery.

Day-to-day

The Dorking is a generally good bird to keep, with an essentially hardy yet placid nature. There are no significant temperament differences across the colour range, although it's worth noting that the Silver Grey can sometimes be a little aggressive, particularly during the mating season or if handling has been minimal.

These birds love to free-range and, perhaps surprisingly considering their size, large fowl Dorkings are pretty good fliers; they'll happily take to the trees if they feel like it. The hens can make good, attentive mothers, but age is a factor in their ultimate reliability. Don't attempt natural incubation with hens that are less than two years old.

While a draught-free housing environment is important for any breed of poultry, it seems especially so for the Dorking. These birds are prone to respiratory problems (including mycoplasma). Colds, sneezes and 'rattly' breathing can all be common occurrences if the birds have to endure poor housing conditions. It must be up to scratch to keep them healthy, with plenty of ventilation but no draughts. What's more, these conditions should be maintained all year round. Don't imagine that you're doing them a favour by shutting all the vents during winter weather, because they'll suffer. A good

airflow through the house must be maintained.

Shelter is important, too. This tendency towards respiratory complaints means that Dorkings can suffer unnecessarily if they're allowed to get wet and cold. Unfortunately, they aren't the cleverest birds around, and have been known to simply stand and get wet if there's no obvious shelter around.

Clean bedding is another vital requirement. Once again, although this should be a given as far as good husbandry is concerned, Dorkings are even more sensitive than usual to polluting, ammonia-generating effects of dirty and/or sodden house litter. Perch height is an important factor too; it must never be too high because the weight of the large fowl can stress their feet as they jump down, promoting the onset of bumblefoot. Check feet regularly, and use a preparatory treatment such as Stockholm Tar to help prevent any damage. A final word of warning to prospective keepers is that Dorkings seem to be extra sensitive to the effects of red mite infestation – anemia can set in at an early stage if these tiny pests aren't kept under control.

Fertility levels are typically good

Rose comb found on Dark, Cuckoo and White Dorkings should be moderately broad and covered in small, coral-like points of even height. The leader at the back should be distinct and slightly upturned

Female Silver Greys can often show a 'foxy' red-brown colour in the wings, which creeps around from the breast. Male Silver Greys showing any brassy red colouring on their back or hackle feathers will tend to pass this on to females, as seen above

When inspecting Dorking feathering, look for full, wide feathers in the wing and tail

A well-marked Silver Grey Dorking male's wing showing blue/green sheen on coverts. Split wings, where the primary feathers droop down lower than they should when the wing is folded, are something to be avoided

among young birds, but it will fall away dramatically with birds older than three years. The females tend to come into lay early in the year (January) but males are often slower, needing a bit of sun on their backs before they get going (March/April). If you're aiming to produce birds for exhibition then you'll have to hatch early (never later than May) to ensure the youngsters have

enough time to reach maturity before the big winter shows.

Chicks tend to be strong and healthy straight out of the shell so you should encounter few problems. However, watch out for feather-pecking among youngsters, especially if space is limited. They'll need to be kept occupied to avoid any bad behaviour; use fresh turfs/greens, wild bird seed bells, pecker blocks, etc, to offer distractions.

If you are not interested in breeding, and simply want to keep a few Dorking hens as a source of eggs, then you can expect 150 a

season from a healthy young hen. They will usually maintain this production rate for about three years (all else being equal), then numbers will fall away. The eggs themselves will be medium-sized and white-shelled if the birds are pure breeds. If not, they'll be slightly tinted. Then, of course, there's always the meat aspect to be considered.

As increasing numbers of poultry keepers are beginning to think about the option of rearing a few birds for the pot – as an alternative to the supermarket-supplied, chemically-enhanced alternative – the Dorking springs to mind as a very useful all-rounder. Plenty of meat, relatively easy to keep, reasonably productive as a layer and very interesting from a conservation point of view. What's more, with the five colour options available, there should be something in the range to suit most tastes!

Dark Dorking hen with rose comb. Note typical massive body, short legs and very good overall type

YES OR NO?

✔ Ancient roots.
✔ Docile nature.
✔ Utility performance.
✔ Great table bird.

✘ Risk of respiratory problems.
✘ Limited supply.
✘ Bantams very scarce.

Dutch bantam

Yellow partridge males certainly have spectacular plumage

Despite its outward delicacy, the Dutch bantam represents a surprisingly robust and practical proposition

It has been suggested that the Dutch bantam, in its gold partridge form, is just about as close as you can get in visual terms to the daddy of them all, the red Jungle Fowl. It's also a member of that elite group of breeds, the true bantams – a handful that are naturally small and so have no large fowl counterpart.

In common with other members of the group, including the Sebright, Pekin and Rosecomb, the Dutch wasn't 'bred-down' to this size like, for example, the bantam version of the Sussex. This friendly, jaunty little bird is a stand-alone breed in its own right and, despite being a relative newcomer to the UK, has generated a firm and enthusiastic following among an ever-growing number of keepers and admirers.

Dutch traders

The breed's specific routes aren't known, but it's thought that traders brought the original bantam back from the Dutch East Indies; the story goes that the birds were used on the ships as a source of fresh meat and eggs; the combination of its diminutive stature and good laying performance proved a winner in the cramped condition on board.

Once in Holland the bantam was inevitably subject to some crossing with indigenous farmyard fowl, and the development process began. The breed was first recognised by the Dutch Poultry Club in 1906, and there are suggestions that a rose-combed variant existed early on too, although all traces of this seem to have vanished.

Despite now being an extremely popular breed in Holland, the

C

D

E

B

A

F

Dutch didn't start appearing at exhibitions as a show bird until the 1950s, though the first documented reference to the breed appeared way back in the early 1880s. It's also surprising to note that the breed took until the late 1960s to find its way across the North Sea and into the UK.

A breed club for the Dutch was formed here in 1982, which continues successfully to oversee the wellbeing of the 13 standardised colours approved by the Poultry Club of Great Britain. Currently, in the Netherlands, there are 24 recognised colour variants. Although there are as yet no plans to standardise additional colours in the UK, there are certainly plenty of breeders who are working to create new variations, either by importing stock from the Netherlands or by crossing existing colours.

G

M

L

K

J

A good number of these alternative colours are now being exhibited around the country, and are gaining recognition in the 'non-standard colour' classes. Of the current standardised colours, it's the gold partridge and silver partridge which continue to be the most popular among keepers and exhibitors, although we gather from the club that all the other variants are kept currently by members, in varying numbers.

Good proposition

The generally widespread appeal of the Dutch bantam works in its favour as far as stock availability is concerned. According to experienced breeder and true bantam judge Peter Tasker, there are good birds available for sale in all areas of the country. As with anything else, there's plenty of rubbish awaiting the unwary buyer. All sorts of things are getting tagged as 'Dutch' these days, but quality varies wildly.

The breed is ably supported by the active and enthusiastic Dutch Bantam Club, which contains many breeders of top-quality stock. A telephone call to the secretary should put you in touch with a nearby supplier, and this is the only purchase route that we'd recommend, especially for those new to the breed.

The Dutch is characterised by its generally upright

A Wattles should be bright red, finely-textured, small and round. Avoid those, which are obviously pendulous, unevenly sized or not predominantly flat.

B The beak should be short, straight and slightly curved. Its colour should be dark grey colour, to match the bird's legs in most plumage colours. However, the white, cuckoo and cuckoo partridge birds should feature a lighter, pinky-white colour on both beak and legs.

C Comb should be bright red, upright and straight with, ideally, five evenly-spaced points. The points number can vary quite a lot, so check carefully. Its size should be in proportion with the head; not too small or big.

D A 'flyaway' tendency like this at the rear of the single comb is perfectly acceptable. Combs that flop to one side are not. Check for damage on the headgear and around the face. This can be a sign of a bird that fights, which is bad news. Both males and females can be 'fighters', and such birds should be avoided.

E Eyes should be large and bright and coloured orange-red to brownish-red. Avoid dark brown or black eyes, as well as those which are far too light.

F Ear lobes should be white, oval and completely free from red or pink discolouration. However, any sign of white on the face of a young bird is a fault. While it can occur as birds get older, finding it on a youngster is a serious exhibition fault.

G The back needs to be short, and should ideally form the base of a smooth U-shape between the neck and tail.

H Well-developed and wide sickle feathers are a primary characteristic of the Dutch bantam male. They are an important contributor to the generally abundant look of the feathering on these birds.

I Many Dutch bantam males fall short as far as sickle feather length is concerned. It's important that they form a graceful arc to this sort of degree.

J Saddle hackle feathers should be abundant and flowing.

K Legs should be well spaced but short and free from feathers. Avoid birds with knock-knees and legs that are the wrong colour.

L Wings are large for the size of bird, hence the flying ability. They should be held tight to the body and angled towards – but not touching – the ground.

M Breast should be carried high and well rounded, contributing to the bird's generally upright, jaunty carriage.

and alert stance, short back (forming the base of a U-shape between the neck and tail), broad shoulders, slightly sloping saddle (short and broad) with abundant hackles running smoothly into the tail coverts.

The breast should be prominent, full and carried high, while the wings are relatively large and long, but not too pointed. These are carried low and close to the body. The tail is upright, full and well spread, with at least eight pairs of well-developed, wide and curved sickle feathers on the male bird.

The head is small and the face is red and smooth. The single, upright and straight comb is relatively small, should present five serrations and tends towards the flyaway type. The beak is short, strong, and slightly curved, while the eyes are large and lively. Wattles should be fine-textured, short and round, and the ear lobes are pure white, small, fine and oval or almond-shaped.

The head sits on top of a short, curved and finely tapered neck with plentiful hackle feathers, and the bird itself stands on well-spaced and straight legs. The thighs are short, as are the shanks which are also free from feathers. Each foot has four, well-spread toes.

The Dutch bantam is famed for luxuriant plumage that lies close to the body and is notable for the plentiful sickles, side hangers and coverts. The general characteristics of the female are similar to those of the male, allowing for the natural sexual differences.

Tough cookie

Considering the tiny size of the Dutch, you may be surprised that it's a very hardy breed that will happily withstand cold and frost, as long as it's kept dry. According to Peter Tasker, you'll often find these resilient little birds preferring to roost in the open at night, rather than take the cosy option inside the hen house.

This useful level of hardiness helps ensure that these birds are easy and straightforward to keep. Food consumption is low compared to the average large fowl. But one downside, particularly for inexperienced keepers, is that these birds are good fliers, and will clear any fence with ease. So, unless you

The difference between good and bad gold partridge female markings. The bird on the right is showing much darker, better peppering across the back, wings and shoulders

AT A GLANCE

Size
True bantam

Origin
Holland

Weights
Male - 500-550g (18-20oz)
Female – 400-450g (14-16oz)

Egg laying
200+ pa

Colours
Gold partridge, silver partridge, yellow partridge, blue silver partridge, blue yellow partridge, blue partridge, red-shouldered white, cuckoo partridge, cuckoo, black, white, blue, lavender

intend keeping them in an aviary-style, closed run environment, it's important to rear them with plenty of regular handling to ensure they become tame and happy in the environment you create. In this

way, even if they do take off into nearby trees, the chances are that they'll return when they're ready to. But it's not all bad news; this impressive flying ability can prove a real asset in terms of dodging predators like cats, dogs and even foxes.

The Dutch is certainly a jaunty bird that's full of character. Consequently it's well suited to a domestic environment, and will handle confinement well if necessary and appropriate. It's worth noting, though, that the male birds can sometimes be feisty, and definitely won't shy away from tackling other birds, cats and even dogs if provoked. For this reason, males together can be problematic, unless they've been reared as a group. What's more, their size can make them vulnerable to damage from larger birds if run in a mixed flock. The often pugnacious nature of the males means they'll tend to

The good, 'blocky' colouring of this gold partridge male is what's necessary to produce well-marked young male offspring

have a go a much larger male birds, despite the risk of injury to themselves.

Good breeder

The Dutch bantam is an easy bird to breed. The hens lay a lot of eggs (200+ through the year) and fertility levels are typically high. The females will go broody but they don't tend to make the best mothers. Boredom seems to creep in a few weeks after hatching, and there's a danger that the adult will either desert or attack the youngsters, particularly male chicks. For these reasons, most serious breeders use incubators and brooder units to hatch and raise their stock. This approach shouldn't throw-up many problems as the chicks tend to be hardy and grow-on strongly.

This breed is a popular show bird, with the gold partridge being one of the most popular exhibition colours. However, breeding good examples isn't simply a matter of pairing-up the best male and

The slight 'fish tail' showing between the second and third comb spikes from the right on this gold partridge male would be enough to cause it to be disqualified by a show judge

female you have. The relative plainness of the gold partridge female (basically brown with dark

peppering over the back, wings and tail), means that a good one needs to be mated with a poor male to ensure that the simplicity of the hen's plumage is maintained. Using a brightly-coloured, well-marked male will simply transfer aspects of this colouring into the female offspring, which is undesirable from a showing point of view.

The opposite applies when breeding for exhibition males, when the best male must be used to ensure that good colour is passed on into the male offspring. Another important point to note, if you're keen on the exhibition prospects of this breed, is that the Dutch is only a one-year bird as far as showing is concerned. Once the first set of adult feathers have moulted out, the tail and wing feathers that replace them are shorter and narrower than the originals, so second-year birds will never do as well in competition. However, although the feather quality deteriorates, good examples will remain very useful as breeding stock.

Getting started with Dutch bantams needn't be expensive either. Individual, well-bred birds can be bought for £15-20 at current prices (2009), but most people tend to buy them in trios of one male and two females, for which you should expect to pay about £50 from a respected breeder. What's more, with a typical lifespan of five years (though many birds living on well past this) these personable little bantams are perfectly capable of offering a great deal of fun and interest for the whole family over a good length of time. •

Dutch females must present a well-fanned tail; never whipped

YES OR NO?

✔ **Surprisingly hardy.**
✔ **Friendly.**
✔ **Great range of colours.**
✔ **Good fertility levels.**

✘ **Enthusiastic flyer.**
✘ **Males can be feisty.**
✘ **Lots of substandard stock around.**

Faverolles

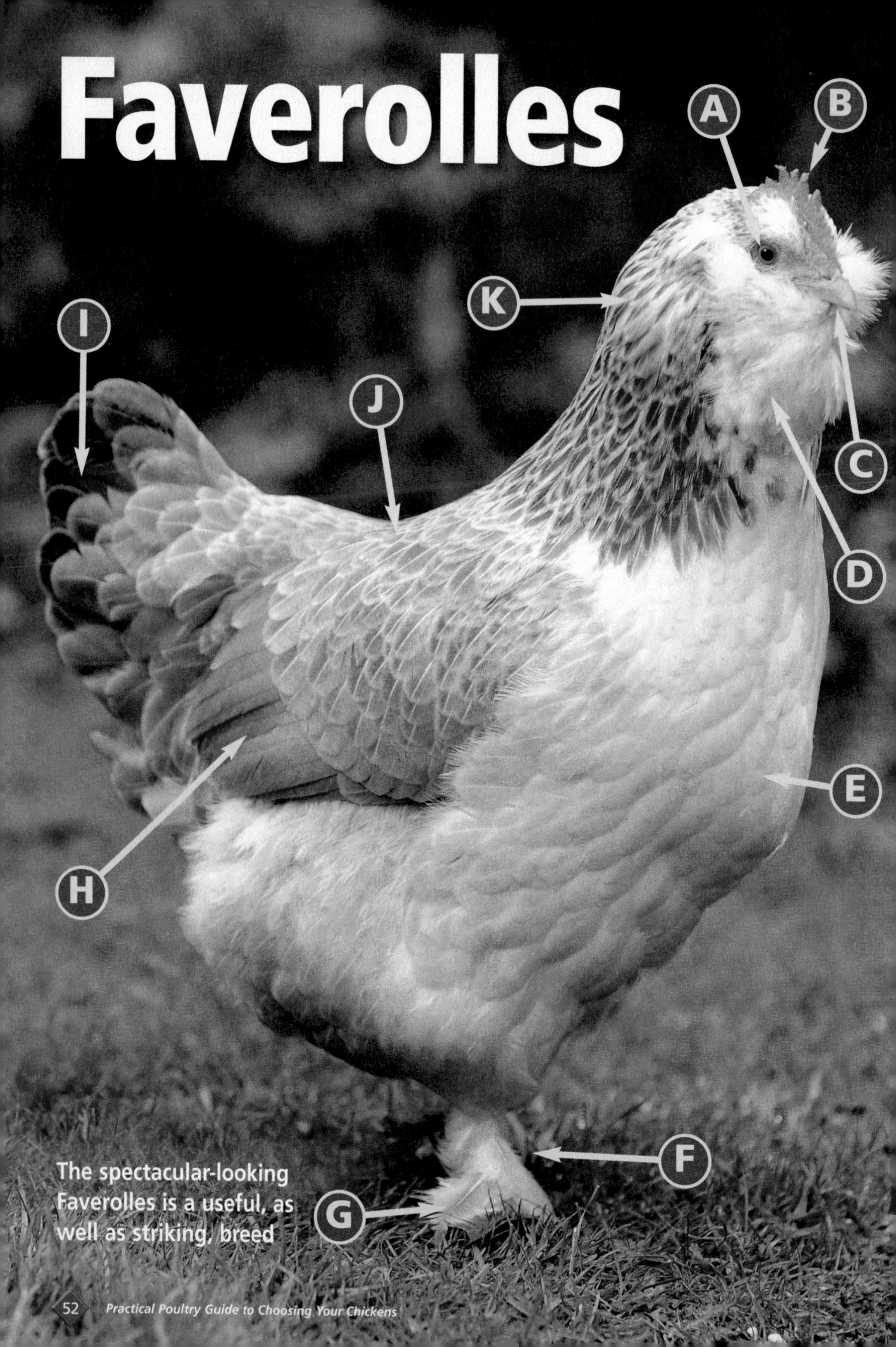

The spectacular-looking
Faverolles is a useful, as
well as striking, breed

A Eyes should be prominent and not obscured by the muffling. Colour is important from an exhibition point of view, as explained in the main text. Avoid birds showing pale eye colour if you're hoping to show; this is a minor exhibition fault.

B Comb shouldn't be too large, and certainly not floppy. Side sprigs are a serious fault and, ideally, there should be between four and six serrations. Combs are proportionately smaller on the female, as seen here. They should be smooth and red on both sexes, as should the ear lobes, wattles and face. Any white in the lobes should be avoided.

C The Faverolles has a short, stout beak which should be white or horncoloured on the buff, cuckoo, ermine, salmon (as here) and white. On black and laced blue examples it should be black.

D The muffling is an important factor that accounts for 10% of the available points in an exhibition situation. It's more pronounced on female birds, and the key points are that it should be full, wide, short and solid. Absence of muffling can result in disqualification.

E A good Faverolles female should show a longer and deeper keel bone than a male, but the breast itself should never be too rounded. On salmon birds, white or brown in breast should be avoided. A crooked breast bone will result in show disqualification.

F It's important that the legs aren't too feathered. The breed standard calls for sparse feathering down the outside of the shanks and on to the outer toe. The presence of vulture hocks or excessive foot feathering are serious exhibition defects, as are knocked-knees.

G Toe spacing is another important Faverolles requirement. The front three should be well spread and straight, while the two at the rear need to be quite distinct from each other, with one on the ground, and the other turned upwards. Birds without five toes will be disqualified from an exhibition.

H Wings are small but prominent in the front, carried rather high and well tucked in. Wings carried low are not a good feature.

I Tail angle is another important consideration; it needs to be 'somewhat upright' on male birds and 'midway between upright and drooping' on the female. Tails on young males can look rather too high to begin with, but they generally drop when the mature feathers appear. Avoid flowing tails.

J Back tends to be longer on the female than the male. Look for good width across the shoulder and saddle. Avoid buff birds with a 'cushion' of feathers ahead of the tail as this suggests Orpington or Pekin in their genetic make-up.

K The female Faverolles tends to have a straighter neck than the male. Hackle feathers on the female salmon will be laced with cream, as here.

The attractive Faverolles is a good example of what's known as a 'composite breed'; one that was created by a program of careful cross-breeding. The influx of Asiatic fowl during the mid-1800s presented the most imaginative poultry keepers in Europe and North America with exciting breeding opportunities. They were able to cross these exotic birds from the Far East with their existing stock, to create a range of high-performing 'new' breeds including the Rhode Island Red, Wyandotte, Plymouth Rock, Barnevelder, Marans and Welsummer.

The objective with the Faverolles – which takes its name from the village in Northern France where it was developed during the first half of the 19th century – was to produce a genuinely useful, dual-purpose utility fowl; a heavy, white-fleshed table bird offering good laying performance too. Essentially, it's thought to have been created by crossing the Houdan – a native of this region of Northern France – with the Dorking from the UK. But various historical accounts hint at the involvement of other breeds as well, including the Cochin, Brahma and Malines (a Belgian breed). Ultimately, of course, nobody can be completely sure.

Utility merit

What most agree on is that the result represents a robust, dual-purpose bird with plenty going for it. The first examples crossed the Channel to the UK in 1895, although their greatest fans at that stage were likely to have been members of the English aristocracy – in those days poultry showing was very much a rich man's pursuit. The birds began to be shown here just before the First World War and then, during the inter-war years, started to be entered in laying trials, with a considerable amount of success. They also started to become quite popular as a meat bird, although their feathered legs were apparently a bit of an issue for some people.

The Faverolles really does present a unique appearance and, fittingly, breeders have adopted their own special word to describe its overall shape; 'cloddy'! These birds have a solid body that's broad across the shoulders with a fairly long back. The breast is broad too, and features a deep keel bone. But the wings are small, carried high, held close and tucked in to the body. The head is broad and flat, and features a smooth, single and upright comb with up to six serrations.

One of the Faverolles' most obvious identifying features is the impressive head muffling, which frames the face with a 'whisker and beard' effect and is sufficient to partially obscure the ear lobes and wattles. Other notable facial features include a stout beak and prominent eye.

The Faverolles' tail is moderately long with broad feathers and should be set midway between upright and drooping (it should never be as high as the head). The whole body is supported on shortish, strong and widely-spaced legs that are sparsely feathered down to the outer toe. The feet feature five toes; the front three should be well spread and straight, the fourth rearward-facing and on the ground, while the fifth must be distinctly separated from the fourth, but turned up the leg.

It's thought that salmon and ermine (which is a Columbian-style colour scheme, similar to a Light Sussex) were the first colours to reach the UK, and the salmon remains the most popular version here to this day. However, the salmon birds we have nowadays are somewhat different from those still kept in France. There the breeders maintain two versions; a light and a dark. The Faverolles remains a popular breed in France, although it's interesting to note that they haven't bothered with the bantam version. This was developed by breeders in the UK during the 1950s, and also in Germany. Traditionally the bantam has been more popular here but, in the past five or six years, the large fowl have come more to the fore.

Plenty of choice

The Faverolles boasts an abundance of soft feathers, and there are seven standardised colours to choose from; black, laced blue, buff, cuckoo, ermine, salmon and white. Salmon males should show a good, solid black breast and underside. Beards should be black too, without brown flecks (grey underfluff often shows through). Neck and saddle hackles should be a straw colour without a 'thumb mark' (this often moults out of young birds as they reach maturity, and is usually darker on dark-backed birds). Feathers should be clear of black stippling if possible. Back and shoulders are 'cherry mahogany', which can be interpreted as chestnut brown or reddish brown. A good solid colour is preferable in whatever shade, particularly in young birds. Older ones normally fade with gold streaks and shades.

Salmon females have beautiful creamy breasts, beards and undersides – without any trace of black. Ideally, their backs should be a flat, medium pinky-brown from the base of the neck to the tail, although this is difficult to achieve from a breeding point of view. Very dark or very pale females are not good for exhibition.

On the blue version each feather is laced with dark, blue-grey edging and the neck hackles on male birds are a shiny, dark grey. The buff standard demands an even and rich lemon-buff colour throughout, with the buff colour running right down to the skin.

The two self-colour options – the black and the white – are probably the most straightforward, in pure breeding terms. Blacks should show a lustrous, beetle-

The salmon is the most popular of the seven standardised Faverolles colours. This male presents a typically rich mixture of straw, cherry mahogany, cream and black feathering

The attractive buff is quite a difficult colour to perfect, so is perhaps not the ideal choice for the inexperienced keeper with aspirations in the show pen. The same applies to the laced blue

green sheen across the back and wings, while the white, as you might imagine, is just that.

The emine (a variation on the Columbian colour theme) has a pure white body and beard but with black striping on the neck hackles, black in the flight feathers on the wings and a black tail. Finally, on the cuckoo, each feather has bands of light grey, grey and almost black, ending in a dark tip. Both dark and light cuckoos are acceptable as exhibition birds.

Among these standardised colours there is some variation in eye, beak and leg colour. Eyes are black or dark brown on blues and blacks, but orange, yellow, grey or hazel on salmons and other varieties. Beaks are coloured black on laced blue and black-feathered

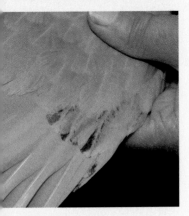

Check buff wings for discolouration. The appearance of black here is not a good sign and is best avoided

Buff undercolour should run right down to the skin

birds, and horn or white on salmon and the other plumage options. Legs and feet are black on black-feathered birds, blue on the laced blue birds and white on all the rest.

Sourcing stock

The British Faverolles Society currently has about 100 members so, overall, the breed's immediate future looks reasonably secure. However, the recent upsurge in demand for the large fowl means that these are currently in rather short supply. Consequently, the situation is better if you're after bantams, with salmon, cuckoo and black all being relatively easy to buy at the moment. Buffs, ermines, blues and whites are a good deal more scarce, though. As far as type is concerned, it's the salmons, cuckoos and blacks that are looking closest to the breed standard.

If you're seriously considering taking on the Faverolles, then it's important to appreciate the physical size of the large fowl; they are big birds and so they need space. Even the bantams are fairly substantial – their weights are usually expressed in pounds rather than ounces – but it's the large version that has the most pressing requirement for adequate room. Keeping these birds in an area that's too small means that they simply won't thrive. As a guide, the Society advises that half a dozen birds will need a run area measuring 30'x30' (9mx9m). Their housing should be on the large size too, for the best results. Sensibly adapted garden sheds can work very well for these birds.

One other important practical requirement is that Faverolles are kept on dry ground. While no chicken will be happy if conditions are damp underfoot, the Faverolles appears rather more sensitive than most to a damp, muddy environment. Apart from this aspect, though, the breed is generally regarded as hardy, and is perfectly capable of dealing with the low temperatures of Northern European winters, assuming that adequate shelter is provided.

Another real plus point is that these birds typically display a lovely, docile character. The bantams, in particular, are especially good with children, making them ideal birds

Foot feathering should be restricted to the outer toe. Toes four and five at the back should be distinct from each other. Keep a wary eye out for scaly leg mite at all times

for a back-garden, family set-up. They are very trusting and easily tamed, so handling is never an issue. As far as large fowl are concerned, you do come across the odd strain where a male bird will be a little feisty (especially in the spring, as the mating season begins), but these are rare. Nevertheless, it's always worth questioning the breeder about the behaviour of the parent stock of any birds you're keen to buy.

Generally speaking, the Faverolles isn't a difficult bird to keep or breed. You can expect fertility levels to be pretty good and the chicks, once hatched, tend to be strong and develop well. However, they're not the fastest

The cuckoo is another favourite colour, with its attractive combination of light grey, dark grey and black banding on every feather

growers, so if you're rearing for the table then bear in mind that this breed certainly won't grow at anything like the same rate as a modern hybrid meat bird. While the large fowl don't make particularly reliable broodies (weight is a problem), the bantams are excellent in this respect, proving to be trustworthy sitters and attentive mothers thereafter.

But if you are intending to use 'natural brooding' as a hatching method, then it's very important that you are sure about whether or not your broody hens have been vaccinated against Marek's disease. If they have the disease then there's a strong risk that they will pass on the disease to the chicks they hatch, which is very bad news. I gather that this sort of vaccination is a rarity in the Society, but birds from other sources may well have been treated differently.

Just about the only other problem you're likely to encounter when keeping Faverolles is caused by scaly leg mite. faverolles, like all other feather-legged breeds, are more prone to this irritating and uncomfortable condition, so bear this in mind with birds you keep

and any you're considering buying. Take time to inspect their legs closely, looking for the tell-tale signs of crusty, grey deposits and raised scales around the base of the feathers.

The Faverolles offers keepers a unique combination of dual-purpose utility value and strikingly unusual looks. They are wonderful birds in the back garden environment, with the bantams

Undercolour on the cuckoo should be pale to medium grey in alternating bands right down to the skin

being especially well suited to households with children. The meat produced is tasty and, traditionally, it's a Faverolles hen that is used in the classic French dish, *petit poussin*. Don't underestimate laying ability either. Not only is the typical yearly total of 180 eggs pretty impressive – even by modern standards – the fact that Faverolles hens will lay well into the winter is another genuine advantage of the breed.

So, if you're looking for an interesting and productive breed to bolster a small flock of backyard fowl, and you have a reasonable amount of space at your disposal, then the Faverolles certainly provides a very worthwhile and practical option.

YES OR NO?

✔ Hardy, docile character.
✔ Attractive and unusual appearance.
✔ Good layer.
✔ Good table bird.

✘ Large fowl need plenty of space.
✘ Scaly leg-mite always a risk.
✘ Some large males can be feisty.

Hamburgh

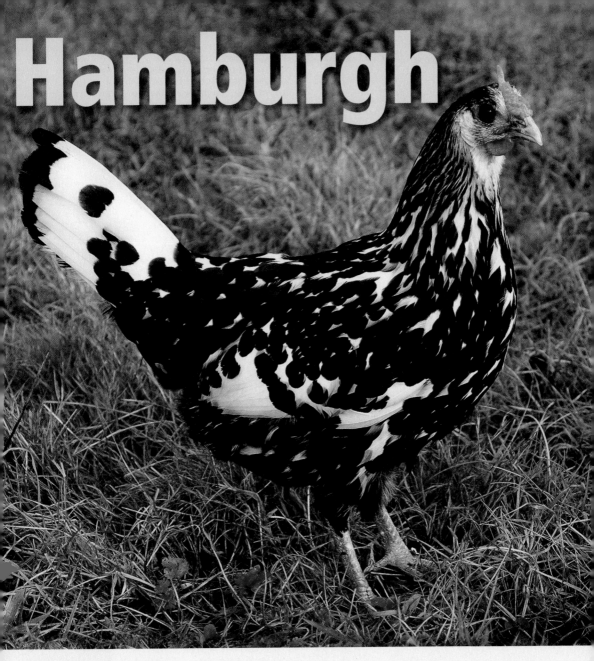

A breed that, despite its Germanic-sounding name, was honed to perfection 150 years ago in Britain

Above: Silver spangled hen

The Hamburgh represents one of the more interesting breeds, from a poultry history point of view, because it was created by what amounts to an exhibition-led decision of convenience. Its history offers a fascinating mix of well-informed cross-breeding, showing excellence and regional loyalties. The result is a bird that many consider to be among the most striking of all; a fowl that possesses levels of grace, dignity and overall beauty that are hard to beat.

The 'Hamburgh' name was adopted as a handy banner under which to group two similar but distinctly different types of chicken that had been developed in different ways but using common ancestry.

On the one hand there's what we now know as the pencilled Hamburgh. It's generally believed that the first versions of this finely-marked bird were imported to this country from mainland Europe, probably Holland (although there are also links with Germany). However, some claim the roots of

Hamburghs aren't the best mixers... even with each other! This is especially so when they're kept in confined conditions. Bear this in mind if you're considering starting with the breed

this pencilled fowl – known originally here as the 'Everlasting Layer' – can be traced much further east, and that it's linked with Turkey or beyond.

Good looking

These birds, when they hit the London markets, were an instant success, not only because of their fine appearance but also due to their laying ability. Although the chalky white-shelled eggs were only medium-sized, laying performance was impressively good for the time. Meanwhile, the second strand of the story was developing in northern England, where breeders worked loyally with their own traditional silver and gold regional breeds. Found in Lancashire and Yorkshire, these included the Bolton Grey, Silver Mooney and Yorkshire Pheasant, and most were either pencilled or spangled. The way things were at that time meant that these birds remained isolated within their regions, although there's evidence to suggest that they were shown informally at a local level.

As the the idea of exhibitions took-off during the mid-1800s, breed classification between those imported from elsewhere in Europe and the

Black Hamburghs are a rarity these days. Good ones will display a prominent beetle green sheen on all feathers

A The rearward-facing spike, or leader, is a very important part of the Hamburgh's rose comb. It should taper to a point at the back, and continue the straight line of the top surface when viewed from the side. Leaders that dip down to follow the line of the neck are a serious fault.

B The rose comb should be square-fronted and feature a level top that's free from hollows or grooves. Top surface should be covered in small, coral-like nobbles, or 'workings'. Avoid combs that droop down on either side to partially cover the eyes.

C The beak is short and well curved, and should ideally be a dark horn colour across all plumage variants apart from the black, when it can be much darker.

D Wattles need to be smooth, rounded and of fine texture. Blacks tend to develop longer, more pendulous wattles with age.

E Eye colour can vary a little but the general rule is as dark as possible. It can range from black to hazel, and dark red can be acceptable, but nothing lighter than this.

F The ear lobe must be rounded, symmetrical and white, and sized in proportion to the rest of the head. Lobe shrivels during the moult, but shape will return afterwards.

G The Hamburgh features long and flowing neck hackle feathers, which extend right down to cover the shoulder. On this silver spangled male, these feathers are pure white and feature small, dagger-like black marks at the tips.

H One of the characteristics of the Hamburgh's bold, alert stance is its well-rounded, prominent breast.

I Legs should be slate blue/grey across all plumage colours. Some exhibition spangled bantams have been suffering with white legs recently, which isn't good. Pink toes on pencilled birds can be another problem to watch for. Avoid birds showing any tendency to be knock-kneed.

J Wings are large and neatly tucked, being held high and close to the body.

K Each sickle is tipped with a black spangle on this silver spangled male. Watch for smuttiness in the tail feathers – white feathers must be pure white.

L Tail should be long and sweeping, with broad sickle feathers and plentiful secondaries. It should be held well up (about 45°) but never too high or squirrel-like.

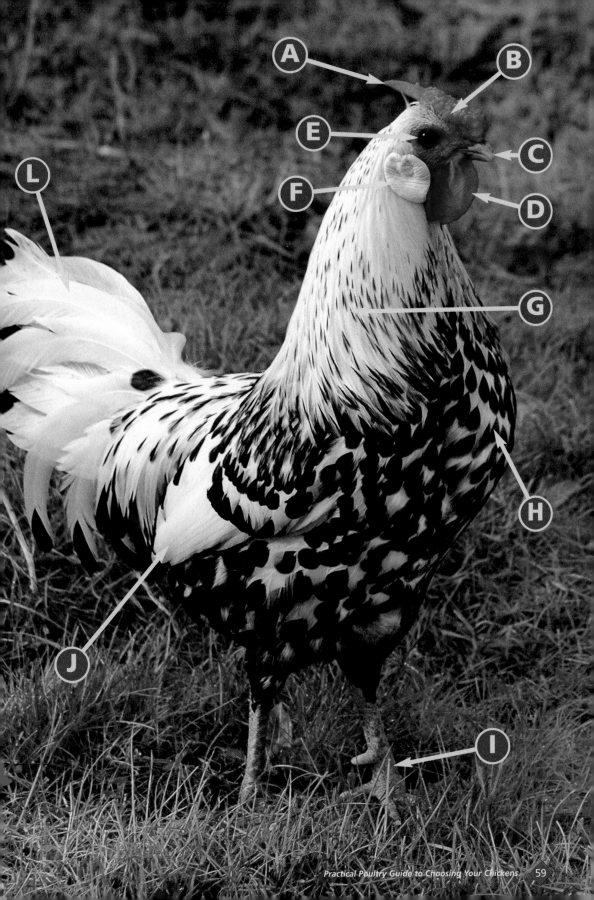

When you see the size of the Hamburgh's wing in relation to its body, it's no wonder that these birds are such good fliers!

indigenous fowl started to cause problems. In this particular case it was decided that the most convenient solution would be to group some of the spangled and pencilled northern breeds with the similar types imported from the Continent (same general type, white ear lobes, coloured legs and rose combs), and call them all 'Hamburghs'.

As things stand now, there is a black version, which was created here, plus gold and silver spangled (also created in the UK). The silver and gold pencilled Hamburghs are based on the European imported fowl, and there are bantam versions of all five types.

All colours are available today, although some are easier to source than others. That said, the Hamburgh is nevertheless a relative rarity and even though the breed club boasts a healthy-sounding 120 members, the actual number of serious breeders producing good

Good pencilled feather marking is spectacular; in this example the whites are good and clear

quality stock in saleable numbers is pretty limited. The most popular type at the moment is the silver spangled bantam. Gold spangled bantams are much in demand too, but finding good examples is trickier – many tend to be too big and too black. In fact, excessive size is a bit of a Hamburgh bantam issue, across all colours. Large fowl blacks are very rare, as are silver pencilled, but large gold pencilled can be sourced more easily.

Parent quality

When buying stock, what a lot of people fail to consider is the quality of the parent stock. Hamburghs are difficult and complicated to breed to standard, so unless you're buying birds from an established strain it's hard to be sure exactly what any subsequent offspring are going to be like. A superb-looking bird may not necessarily produce equally good offspring.

The important point to appreciate is that there's no quick route to success with Hamburghs. Any experienced breeder will tell you that you need to keep and breed from a strain for several years before you can start to be sure about what you've got. Start with the best birds you can get, and resist the temptation to keep adding fresh stock into the breeding mix. Working with Hamburghs requires patience and knowledge; the ability to select good from bad is vital if you're to achieve any sort of useful consistency.

Note that this breed isn't an easy one to exhibit either, especially in its spangled or pencilled forms.

Even the apparently more straightforward blacks can represent a stiff challenge.

Day-to-day

The Hamburgh is undoubtedly best suited to a fairly self-contained, free-range lifestyle. It's a bird that will always do better in all respects with more rather than less space. However, that isn't to say that they can't be confined because they can, assuming all the important welfare and husbandry requirements are met. But, being a light breed these birds are enthusiastic and good fliers. They'll take to the trees given half a chance so Hamburghs being kept in an urban environment will require a secure, roofed run.

In true 'light breed' fashion, the Hamburgh also displays an excitable, feisty character, and while it's possible to calm this temperament with lots of human interaction and careful handling from day one, it's unlikely that you'll ever be able to curb the flighty tendency completely.

Another consequence of this

Poor tip spangling on a silver's primary wing feathers

feisty side to the Hamburgh's character is that, although it's certainly a hardy breed, it's not an ideal bird to run in a mixed flock when in confinement. Even among themselves, Hamburghs can be prone to bullying and feather pecking (the blacks seem particularly prone to the latter). However, with a sensible husbandry approach that takes into account the inherent breed characteristics, these birds shouldn't pose any serious problems.

From a breeding point of view, fertility levels are never usually a problem, and all colours tend to breed well. Large fowl hens don't go broody, so if you're planning the natural approach to hatching you'll need a recognised broody hen for the job. However, bantam versions do seem more inclined to broodiness – especially the gold and silver pencilled versions – although they can be unreliable in the early stages. Once the youngsters have hatched, though, bantam mothers can become fiercely protective of their young.

There's predominantly good news with regard to diseases, in that the Hamburgh is generally pretty resistant to most of the common poultry problems, with the exception of Marek's disease. The pencilled birds seem more prone to this than the other colours but, with careful selection, it is possible to breed this out of a strain given time.

Good comb, leader and dark eye on this silver spangled male

Pretty useful

Few could fail to be won over by the looks of a good Hamburgh. But is this stunning appearance enough to convince would-be keepers that it's worth a go? The breed certainly deserves more attention, that's for sure. Greater numbers of serious keepers are needed to boost overall numbers, but it's not really a bird to be taken on lightly. The Hamburgh demands dedication and skilled selection from its keepers; it's definitely not a breed from which you can normally expect instant exhibition success and, as mentioned earlier, producing stock

to the established standard is no easy task, even for the most experienced of keepers.

But it's not all doom and gloom. The Hamburgh has retained much of the utility quality of its forebears, and remains a useful layer to this day. The black and pencilled versions seem to produce the highest numbers of eggs, with healthy young hens perfectly capable of cracking the 200 barrier. The attractive pure white shells and rich flavour more than make up for any lack of overall size.

Another real plus point is that the Hamburgh is surprisingly long-lived. We've heard tales of black hens living happily into their 11th year, and still producing eggs at that impressive age too! More typically, you can expect most well-managed birds to survive for at least six years. The Hamburgh is a slow-maturing bird and, because overall weights are never that great, it's not known as a table bird, though apparently the meat is succulent, with a slightly gamey flavour.

All in all, then, if you're after an easy life with your hens, then the Hamburgh probably isn't the bird for you. Its flighty nature and feisty character mean it's not the best breed to have around young children, or in an environment where noise and frequent disturbance are a regular feature.

On the other hand, if you have the time and inclination to lavish your birds with dedicated and considered attention – and you relish the challenge posed by breeding these fine birds to the detailed and demanding standard – then the Hamburgh is a thoroughly worthy contender for inclusion near the top of your 'must have' breeds list.

YES OR NO?

✔ **Stunning appearance.**
✔ **Good layer.**
✔ **Hardiness.**
✔ **Good fertility.**

✘ **Flighty character.**
✘ **Enthusiastic flyer.**
✘ **Complicated to breed effectively.**
✘ **Difficult to show.**

Spectacularly marked gold pencilled hen

Indian Game

Some regard it as an 'extreme' breed, but Chris Graham discovers that the Indian game has plenty to offer the discerning keeper

The Indian Game is a breed that never fails to arouse opinion. Some have described it as an 'extreme breed' and, as the bantam versions photographed here illustrate, it's a bird that most people have fairly definite thoughts about.

Love it or loathe it, you've got to admire the Indian Game's purposeful hardiness. Its name throws up all sorts of exotic images from the East but, actually, this breed was created here in the UK about 150 years ago. The story has it that merchants visiting the West Country from the Far East to trade in tin during the mid-1800s brought fighting birds with them – including the Asil and Malay. Local keepers in Cornwall and West Devon took to these exotic breeds, and to the cock fighting aspect too. So much so, in fact, that they started some experimental breeding using the imported birds, in an effort to create an even more effective fighter.

A The neck needs to be of medium length, closely-feathered, curved and elegant. Undercolour should be dark – avoid lightness on Dark Indian Game. White in the hackles, or hackle under-feather, is a no-no.

B The head should be wide when viewed from the front, but not as beetle-browed as a Malay, for example. From the side it should show medium length, but any hint of 'snipeyness' should be avoided. An almost ball-shaped skull is a good thing. Face should be bright red with tight, neat wattles of the same colour.

C Eye should be prominent, with colour ranging from pearl to light red. It tends to lighten with age. Birds with brown or bright red eyes should be avoided.

D A well-defined triple (pea-type) comb as straight as possible – larger on the male birds. The centre ridge should be appreciably higher than those on either side of it. It shouldn't be too big and must be held tight to the head with a bright red colour. Inverted leaders should be avoided (producing a small 'dimple' on the back end of the comb). Large coarse combs should be avoided too.

E Quite a heavy beak, that's well curved with colour ranging from horn to yellow (striped is acceptable).

F Wings should be set fairly high and tight to the body so that the bird has an almost triangular profile when viewed from the front. When viewed from above the body should be broad at the front and taper away towards the base of the tail, resembling a bullock's heart, or flat iron in shape.

G Good depth and roundness to the breast. Feathering should be tight over the whole body and there should be a lack of feathering down the line of the breastbone.

H Feet must have four toes, that are evenly spread and straight, with the rear toe extending backwards and almost flat on the ground. Toenail colour should match the beak.

I Legs should be of an overall length to give the bird a balanced look. There was a fashion 20 years ago for minimising thigh length, which was very bad as it physically limited the birds' ability to breed. A good length thigh is important, but the shank should be shorter. Scaling should be tight and even and the legs should be bright yellow (diet and environment can play a part in this) with large, round bones (needed to support the body weight) – no ridges.

J Thigh length should be enough to ensure the bird has good ground clearance, and that it appears balanced.

K There should be no fluff on an Indian Game, male or female. Hard-feather nature means that the feathers themselves are brittle and easily broken so, if you're interested in showing birds, make sure hen house pop holes are large enough to avoid snapped feathers.

L Tail should be hard and tight, carried in line with the back. Often it'll be held slightly higher than this on bantam versions and while this is not ideal, it's hard to avoid. As long as the tail doesn't sit above the horizontal, this is generally acceptable. Sickle feathers on the male bird should be minimal.

M Back should be flat and relatively short. Some birds can develop muscle growth across the top of the legs, creating a pair of ridges on either side of the back. Avoid this.

Fighting talk

The Malay and Asil fowl were crossed, and then mated with indigenous Old English Game (Oxford type). Unfortunately, as far as the fighting ambitions were concerned, these plans fell rather flat as the bird they created proved to be pretty hopeless as a sporting fowl. On the plus side, though, it was a rugged and massively-boned creature capable of producing impressive amounts of breast meat, and this last characteristic was to prove to be its saving grace; and so the Indian Game was born.

Back in the 1800s chicken was still a luxury food with a correspondingly high value. With this in mind, it wasn't long before the canny West Country breeders started experimenting with their new game bird, by mating it with established white-fleshed, meat-producing utility breeds of the time, such as the Sussex and Dorking. The results were impressive, in terms of meat production, and created what were essentially the forerunners of the modern broiler bird. This lucrative market remained right through until the beginning of the Second World War, and a great many farms in the West Country survived entirely thanks to this trade. At one point Indian Game cocks had a sale value greater than that of a Devon ram or bull.

The breed standard was set in 1886, and a club for owners was established at about the same time. Bantam versions followed in 1899, and are certainly the most popular type among enthusiasts these days. While the Indian Game is a reasonably popular show bird today, historically it has never really caught the imagination of the Fancy in the same way that the 'fluffier' breeds did. The inter-war years probably represented the breed's popularity heyday, when it was widely kept across the UK as a farm bird, still enjoyed a good reputation as a meat-producer and was reasonably popular on the show scene too.

One other notable historical point of interest is that Reginald Appleyard used the Indian Game in his crossing mix which eventually led to the creation of the Ixworth in the early 1930s. This useful bird –

Indian Game hens will produce eggs for a good many years, although the total number laid is never that great. Birds in good health should produce between 80-90 medium-sized, roundish, tinted eggs per season

both for meat and egg production – was developed by breeding Jubilee and white Indian Game, white Sussex, white Orpington and white Minorca. Unfortunately, it never really caught on, and remains a rarity in specialist hands to this day.

Dark beginnings

The original Indian Game colour was the Dark, with its attractive chestnut-brown ground colour and black double lacing. This was followed by the Jubilee – created to commemorate Queen Victoria's Diamond Jubilee in 1897 – which replaced the black lacing with white. The only other standardised colour is the blue, which again has the same rich brown base colour,

The Jubilee colour pattern on a bantam female

but with blue/grey lacing. Although the blue is fairly well-established on the Continent (particularly in Germany), it's never really caught on in the UK and so remains the rarest of the three today (there are perhaps only a handful of keepers with them here at the moment). The original Dark is still the most popular by far.

Buying birds is now a good deal easier than it once was, although it has to be said that the Indian Game is still an uncommon breed, so finding good stock can involve a bit of a hunt. We'd certainly always recommend approaching the breed club as the best way of seeking-out a respected supplier. As far as price is concerned, this is variable depending on the quality of stock. In general, though, expect to pay between £20-40 per bird for both good-quality bantams and large fowl. However, top examples can be worth a lot more.

Indian Game is a pretty hardy breed, although it's worth noting that they can feel the cold due to their hardness of feather, and breeding can be somewhat temperature-sensitive. Overall though, these birds do well in a variety of environments, and love nothing more than to be given the space to free range. The large fowl have big appetites so can cost more to keep than you might expect.

Wattles on the Jubilee (left) are far too large. The Dark here is showing a much better size

Characteristic markings on a male wing, apart from the white patch, which isn't desirable

Head shape is important when it comes to showing; avoid 'snipeyness' as shown by the bird on the left

Traditionally, farmers used to turn them out on to the harvested cornfields, and let them forage happily among the stubble. This need for space is an important consideration for anyone thinking of buying. Indian Game don't tolerate close confinement very well, which is perhaps one of the reasons why the bantam version is more popular today.

The Indian's Asil and Malay roots ensure it's a strong-willed bird, with real character. People who keep them tend to become tremendously loyal, and rarely let them go once they're hooked. The birds 'talk' a lot and will become very friendly if frequently handled. Don't imagine, though, that they can be turned into a 'lap bird', because they can't; they will always maintain an independent streak. This factor, plus their considerable weight and strength, means that the large fowl especially are perhaps not best suited to being around young children.

Easy keeping

Flightiness is not a problem you need worry too much about with Indian Game. These birds are easy to contain, with little more than a three-foot fence being required to keep them enclosed. They tend not to be very inclined to get out and explore, assuming they have enough room in the first place. All-in-all they're a relatively easy breed to keep in basic, practical terms.

Things are rather different from a breeding point of view, however. It's worth appreciating from the outset that, if you intend to breed these birds, you're going to struggle. Even experienced breeders describe the process of producing stock to a good standard as being 'heart-breaking'. Low levels of fertility are at the core of the problem, meaning that hatch rates will generally be low. Male birds can be irregular performers, and it's not unheard of to set 100 eggs and only get two or three chicks from them. Then, of course, there's no guarantee that any of those three will show the all-important Indian Game colour and type.

Breeding requires dedication and a good level of matter-of-factness, in terms of being prepared to cull-out sub-standard examples.

A key Indian Game feature is the broadness of the shoulder. The breed standard demands 'elegance with substance'

INDIAN GAME COLOURS

In all three standardised colours, the female must have an even ground colour of chestnut to mahogany brown. Each feather should be double or triple-laced with black, white or blue/grey, depending on colour classification.

Avoid shaftiness, where the quill of the feather appears too light. Watch for 'mossy' (indistinct) lacing towards the tail. The more defined it is in this area, the better the bird. The same thing also applies at the top of the leg, and the front of the wing butts.

Males should be predominantly black, very shiny with an obvious beetle-green sheen. Wing primaries should show a narrow brown 'rimmage', and the secondary wing feathers need to have brown outer edges so that when the wing is held in the closed position a prominent brown-coloured triangle is visible.

A good breeding male should show some chestnut colouring on the lower back just ahead of the base of the tail. While this is unacceptable in a show bird, it's a very important requirement if you're hoping to breed well-laced females.

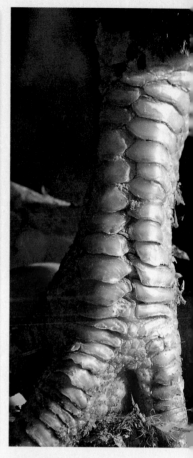

Ridged legs are another bad point. Leg bones should be large, smooth and round

It's also worth noting that any meaningful judgement about an Indian Game's quality can't really be made until the bird is at least six months old; they are slow growers. It's also important not to try to accelerate this early growth because, if birds put on too much weight too early, there's a chance that they may suffer leg muscle problems or even deformities.

With regard to housing, the size and weight of these birds means

Watch out for – and avoid – white undercolour like this on a cock's neck

that perch height is an important issue. It should never be set too high because. Although the birds are perfectly capable of getting on and off a high perch, the action of repeatedly doing so can damage their feet. Consequently, it's best to set the perch height at no more than two feet off the house floor, and to often include an access ramp as well.

Contrary to some reports, bantam hens do make good broody mothers (large fowl aren't so good) and should be able to manage ten eggs quite comfortably. The danger with large fowl is their weight, which means that accidentally broken eggs can be a problem. The breed's hard feathering can work to an advantage in that there's no risk of chick strangulation, as can be the case with more feathery broodies such as the Silkie.

Despite links with a cock-fighting past, the Indian Game isn't known as an aggressive breed. So, while bullying isn't generally a problem that owners should expect,

it can occur if new birds are introduced. Those which have been reared together from scratch should normally be fine, but newcomers to a flock can stir-up trouble. Overall, they're not spiteful birds though, and so can co-exist quite happily with other breeds, under the right circumstances.

The news is good too, as far as disease is concerned. Indian Game aren't particularly prone to any of the common complaints; no more so than any other breed. One thing to bear in mind is that both large fowl and bantams can suffer with mite infestations. Their body shape (in particular, the pronounced shoulder-width) means it's hard for the birds to get their heads round to the vent area, so keepers need to make regular inspections and treat frequently with de-lousing powder etc.

Japanese Bantam

Above: *a frizzle white Japanese bantam female*

One of the fundamental decisions to be made by anyone considering becoming involved with the poultry keeping hobby must relate to the reason for keeping birds in the first place. Essentially, the options can be broken down into three basic categories; for egg/meat production, for exhibition purposes or simply for pure pleasure.

This is a bit of a simplification of course, and there can be a good deal of crossover between these categories. However, there's no doubt that clarifying your own objectives can be a great help when it comes to deciding on the most appropriate breed or breeds to keep.

The Japanese Bantam certainly isn't a bird that you'd keep for any sort of utility reason. But it definitely is one that can be kept purely for pleasure, be it in the domestic back garden environment or a more serious showing-based situation.

True pleasure!

Being one of the exclusive group of true bantams, the Japanese has no large fowl counterpart. It's a unique breed with a character and appearance all of its own, and an Oriental history that goes back deep into the mists of time.

Despite the name, this breed's origins are rooted firmly in China, where the earliest records show that

A brown-red male of good type but lacking in breast lacing

A The Japanese bantam tends, proportionally, to have a rather large, stout head. Face should be bright red, smooth and free from feathers. Take care to avoid white in the ear lobe. This was more of a problem a few years ago across the colour range, but is less common today. Wattles bright red.

B The colour of the strong, curved beak varies with plumage colour. Normally it will be yellow, but flashes of black can occur on a cuckoo, for example. A solid black beak is wrong.

C Male birds should have a large, single comb with four or five, evenly-spaced serrations. Avoid birds with too many spikes – they can have up to nine – or spikes which are 'spindly'. In some cases, the comb can become too large on older males, so that it starts to fold over. Avoid this too. Female combs are generally much smaller but, where larger combs are present, it's perfectly acceptable for these to fold over to one side or the other. It's unlikely that this characteristic will breed-through to male birds.

D Eye should be large, clear and prominent. Colour varies with plumage, from orange through to red. Tend to be duller colour in younger birds.

E Japanese bantam has a very short back which, on a mature male, is covered by the neck hackles, creating a v-shape between neck and tail. Females show a softer u-shape at this point.

F Male tail should be large and upright, with a pair of gracefully curved sickle feathers which extend the overall height significantly. The female tail should stand upright too, and be fairly full, spread and with feathers of an even length. Watch for extremes – too tight or too spread. Tail angle is important too. Squirrel, wry and dropped tails should be avoided.

G Main tail feathers stand upright and should rise above the level of the head. Soft side hangers should also feature on either side.

H Plumage should be dense. Narrow feathers can occur in tail and wing. It's a soft-feathered breed so there should be a profusion, but not to the point of being fluffy. If feathering is too soft then important tail structure can be lost, and the whole effect becomes too droopy.

I Wings are held tight to the body and are fairly long. They should brush along the ground. Don't worry if you find wing feathers frayed at the tips; this is actually the sign of a bird with good carriage.

J Ideally there should be no leg showing at all, just the odd toe sticking out from under the body. Foot and leg colour should match the beak, so predominantly yellow. Some black peppering on the legs is allowed on the blacks and cuckoos, but the underside of the feet must be yellow. Watch out for green-coloured legs on brown-red birds.

K Breast should be round and prominent on both sexes. Body must be short in length (front to back), wide across the shoulder, rounded and 'cobby'. Body must be low to the ground and not high at the front. Neck is fairly short, when the legs are too. Ideally, the head should rise to about two-thirds the height of the tail, on both male and female birds.

examples were bred for the pleasure of the Emperor, and used to grace the gardens of the Royal Palace. The history is traceable right back to the Tang Dynasty (618- 907AD) which was, appropriately enough, the golden age of art in ancient China.

These highly-prized bantams remained exclusively in China until the turn of the 13th century, when examples started finding their way into Japan. However, another 600 years elapsed before Europe was to see the breed, with the first birds being traded into Germany during the 1800s. But UK breeders and enthusiasts didn't get their hands on them until 1860, when they started arriving direct from Japan. Even so, it took a further 50 years for the breed to make its first appearance in a show pen, in 1910.

But the wait was most certainly worth it, as the Japanese Bantam presented a unique appearance combining shortness of leg, small, cobby body, large, single comb and impressive, upright tail. These birds, in fact, have the shortest legs of any poultry breed, and it's these which characterise the breed's dwarfish appearance. They also ensure it has a very distinctive, waddling gait when walking

Those interested in buying Japanese bantams today have plenty of choice, not only as far as colour is concerned, but in terms of feather type too. You can specify standard, frizzle or silkie feathering, although it must be realised that the latter two remain very rare and something of a specialist interest among even the established keepers.

The plain-feathered variety is the original, and certainly remains the most popular among enthusiasts. To illustrate

the point, the Japanese Bantam Club's main show, at Newbury each year, typically attracts about 200 entries. Of these, 185 will usually be plain-feathered birds, ten will be frizzled and the remaining five will be silkies.

The choice between these three is very much a matter of personal preference, of course, but the general consensus is that it's the plain feathering that shows the breed at its best. Important aspects such as the high tail and prominent, smoothly rounded breast can be somewhat diminished by either frizzle or silkie feathering. However, this does tend to be the purists' view, and it remains the case that these two less popular feather options can certainly offer very attractive and unusual choices for keepers seeking a characterful bird with a difference.

Silkie feathering can cause the Japanese to lose some of its identity, which is why most people prefer the original type

Colours galore

There are currently more than 20 colour options available, but the number is increasing all the time as club members strive to create new variations. The most popular and traditional choices – such as the black-tailed white, the blacktailed buff, the white and the black – are bolstered by a selection of greys, mottleds and blues. These are further augmented by the range of colours available with the Old English Game – brown-red, blue-red, silver and golden duckwing etc. For some strange and unexplained reason, a link was forged between the Japanese and the Old English Game in respect of plumage colour. Consequently, any combination which exists for OEG is equally acceptable on the Japanese bantam.

The black-tailed white is still probably the most popular of all the Japanese colours; people seem to love the pure simplicity of its markings. The black is a popular show bird, but isn't so highly regarded among more domestic keepers, who tend to prefer whites for the back garden environment.

If you have ambitions in the show pen, and are planning to breed your own examples for that purpose, then you should appreciate from the outset that the Japanese bantam certainly isn't the easiest exhibitor's breed. These

birds are difficult to breed to a consistently high standard, and it really can come down to a numbers game if you're after top quality offspring.

Poor fertility levels can be the first hurdle to overcome – some males are simply infertile. Then there's the shortness of leg, which can be an equally debilitating issue for male birds too. While being a desirable feature as far as the breed standard is concerned, males can be affected by this to such an extent that they find it hard, sometimes impossible, to 'perform' with the females. For this reason, some experienced breeders make use of longer-legged male birds in their carefully controlled breeding pens.

The Japanese bantam's body must be wide at the shoulder. This, combined with its overall shortness, creates a 'cobby' feel

Gene troubles

Genetics is a further consideration, as the Japanese bantam carries what's known as a lethal gene. This gene, which controls leg length, is passed on to the offspring by both parents, and it's the resultant gene pairing which has the potential to cause real problems. Basically, there are two versions of the gene – one which produces the short leg and one which produces a longer leg. The 'short leg' gene is dominant so, if the embryo receives one of each type, then the bird will have short legs. If it receives two 'long leg' genes then, obviously, the resultant bird will have long legs. However, if the embryo should receive two 'short leg' genes, then this is a lethal combination, and it simply won't survive the incubation period.

It's possible to generalise about these gene pairings using the basic laws of probability. So, on average, 50% of embryos will receive one of each gene, resulting in short-legged offspring. Of the remainder, 25% will receive a pair of 'long-leg' genes to produce long-legged offspring, and 25% will receive two 'short-leg' genes that will cause death in the shell at around day 18.

As a rule of thumb, you should expect only about half of the eggs collected to be fertile. When you then factor-in the consequences of the lethal gene, plus the many other variables that can affect the incubation and hatching process, breeders should be prepared to produce, at best, just a handful of

This black-tailed white is showing some black in its neck hackles. Watch for this when buying. It's likely that this bird is reverting to the Columbian colour pattern

What price?

Japanese bantams can be quite expensive to buy, although the price variations seen tend to relate to quality rather than plumage colour. At one end of the scale, at 2008 prices, it's perfectly possible to buy 'garden stock' for as little as £2-3 a bird. But those looking to source good quality, exhibition type examples should expect to pay £30-40 for a pair or trio from a reputable source. Bearing in mind the sort of numbers needed to give yourself half a chance of setting up a successful breeding program, you can start to appreciate that there can be significant expense involved in getting started.

Despite its small size, the tiny Japanese bantam can offer a good level of hardiness, although it should be noted that this is entirely dependent on feather type. Examples with normal, flat feathering will certainly be hardy enough to run around outside all year around. But the same certainly

good quality birds from every 100 eggs set. With this in mind, the advice from the Japanese Club is that you'll need to work with at least 15 of any one colour if you're making a serious attempt at producing show-quality stock. You can improve your odds of success by breeding with 'compatible' colours – such as black x blue or cuckoo x black – but anyone interested in attempting this really should consult an experienced breeder before they begin. One of the arts of successful Japanese breeding is knowing which birds to pair-up for the best results. A specialist breeder will certainly be able to give you a head start in this respect, by selling you pairs or trios that will be expertly matched, and most likely to produce the sort of offspring you're after.

Too much plain white in the wing is a factor to check for with mottleds. The fraying and discolouration on the feather tips is caused by contact with the ground – a good sign in these short-legged birds

isn't true of the rarer frizzle and silkie varieties. These sorts of feathering leave the birds vulnerable to the wet (their feathers provide less water resistance) and, in turn, to becoming chilled. This is a very

Black-tailed buff female; an attractive colour but quite rare these days

serious condition for small birds like these, and will result in death if action isn't taken. For this reason, frizzle and silkie versions are not terribly well suited to the outdoor life in climates like ours.

These problems can be compounded by the short-legged nature of the breed. With legs that, on a good example, are typically little more than an inch long, there's almost no clearance between the body and the ground. For this reason, keeping dry can become impossibility for birds living in freerange conditions when the ground is often wet. Keepers need to be particularly aware in this respect, and to ensure that their birds have easy access to a poultry house that's completely dry at all times.

Family fun!

But if all that sounds a little daunting, don't let yourself be put off from making the effort because this breed has so much else to offer. After all, if the exhibition scene isn't your thing, then a few examples with legs a little longer than they should be isn't the end of the world.

Well-reared Japanese banties will provide friendly, tame and trusting companions. They'll be easy to handle, non-aggressive and very garden-friendly, making them just about the ideal family bird. The fencing around their run can be kept to a minimum as flighty examples are relatively rare (some of the longer-legged birds can launch themselves at nearby trees) and, of course, there won't be a pressing need for acres of space.

The relatively docile nature ensures that the Japanese bantam is an easy breed to keep. Assuming good levels of basic husbandry, these birds don't suffer from any specific problems or diseases but can be prone to parasitic infestation if routine care and attention is lacking. Thankfully, there's nothing really serious waiting in the wings to strike them down.

Egg production isn't one of the Japanese's strong points. Totals will vary dramatically from strain to strain (plumage colour makes no difference), but even the best are unlikely to top 100 in a season. At worst a hen could produce as few

No, it's not sitting down! This black-tailed white female illustrates how the shortness of leg means that ground clearance is virtually zero!

Here's the difference between a good, short leg (left) and one that's too long, as far as the breed standard is concerned

as 20! As with any other type of poultry, correct diet plays a big part in maximising egg-laying efficiency.

The females make great mothers and are good sitters too; so good, in fact, that some keepers actually prefer them to the legendary Silkie!

So, apart from the labour-intensive and potentially disheartening breeding process, there really isn't much on the downside of owning Japanese bantams. They will add a touch of Eastern spice to any garden, and have the potential to bring colour and character to your life in a way that few other breeds can match. •

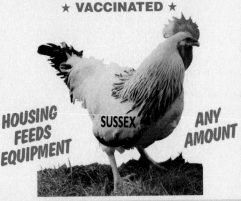

Leghorn

A

B

C

D

E

F

K

I

J

One of the most historically influential breeds there's been, in terms of its effect on the commercial market, and one that continues to represent a great keeping option today

The Leghorn has been an extremely influential chicken over the years. It originated in Italy as one of the white ear-lobed Mediterranean breeds, and found favour in several other European countries due to its laying prowess. But it was in America that the Leghorn was most extensively developed.

The first brown examples were exported there during the 1830s, and it's thought that they took their name from the Italian port of Ligorno, from where the ships departed. White versions followed soon after, and it was these which were the first to come back across the Atlanti, some 40 years later, though only as far as Britain.

Breeders in the USA used the Leghorn as the basis for a number of important breeding programs, including one that resulted in the creation of the Rhode Island Red. However, the first birds that arrived

A Beak should be strong, short, stout and coloured yellow (horn on black birds). Some mottling is acceptable. The front edge of the comb should not extend beyond the tip of the beak, when viewed from the side. 'Open beak' is another condition to be avoided, where the top and bottom bills meet at the tip but they fail to touch further back and a gap is clearly visible.

B Across all plumage colours the eye should be as red as possible. Eye colour will often be lighter and more orangey in young birds, only darkening to the proper red when maturity is reached (POL in hens). Green eyes do occur, but should be avoided if you're intending to exhibit.

C The comb should have up to seven, evenly-serrated points, although five is really the ideal in exhibition terms. It should be straight and upright on cockbreeding strain males, and hanging to one side with a single fold on females. A double-folded comb on a hen is a serious fault.

D The face should always be bright red, matching the comb and wattles on both male and female birds, irrespective of plumage colour. White anywhere on the face is a serious fault, and should be avoided when buying. Wattles should ideally be of an even length and crease-free. There is no set length for them, although they need to balance with the comb – big comb, big wattles!

E Ear lobes should be opaque white in colour and the shape of an almond and free from 'dishing'. They shouldn't be too large either, otherwise they will lose the almond shape and it's also likely that white will start appearing elsewhere on the face; a serious exhibition defect. Thickness and texture are important points too. Thin lobes tend to promote undesirable redness.

F Body wants to be wide at the shoulder, with an obvious and gradual taper back towards the tail. There needs to be a good length to it as well (when viewed from above) as it's a laying breed. The back should be long but in proportion to the rest of the bird.

G Male birds will tend to carry the tail at a slightly higher angle than the 45° typically shown by a good female. The male tail should also feature a set of multiple furnishings (about seven is ideal), including a couple of sweeping sickles. In contrast, a Leghorn hen's tail is much tighter (whipped).

H The black tail of a brown Leghorn like this one should show a beetle green sheen in bright sunshine. Any white showing in the tail feathers is a problem.

I The wings on all Leghorns are large – they are good fliers – but held tightly to the body, and well tucked-up. Always spread the wing of a prospective purchase to check feather quality and colouring.

J Legs and feet should be yellow or orangey-yellow, but definitely not white. Leg colour will gradually fade during the laying season. Some even show a green tinge to them which is best avoided. Black and blue birds can suffer with dark flecking on the legs. This isn't acceptable from an exhibition point of view, but doesn't really matter for the enthusiast keeper. However, it's important to note that leg mottling on young birds will usually clear as maturity approaches. Also avoid flat-shinned legs; they should be round. Four toes on each foot. Watch for bent toes – often the middle toe on large fowl.

K The breast should be round, full and prominent. Take time to handle a bird you're looking at, and check the shape of its breast bone; it should be straight.

back in the UK during the 1870s were thought by many to be too small, so breeders here wasted little time in boosting the size of the white by crossing it with Minorca and Malay strains.

The breed has also played a crucial role in the development of many of the modern hybrid layers and was, at one time, the mainstay of the British commercial laying flock.

Striking headgear

The Leghorn's striking appearance is dominated by its large single comb, which should always stand proudly upright on male birds, but falls to one side on the females. The breed presents an attractively-proportioned, firm and well-feathered body, which is wide at the shoulder and narrows towards the tail. The back is reasonably long and slightly sloping, while the breast is full and prominent. Tails are moderately full and typically held at an angle of 45°, with male birds featuring a handful of sweeping sickle feathers.

Keepers are spoilt for choice when it comes to Leghorn colouring, and can choose from 15 standardised versions including: white, black, brown, blue, buff, cuckoo, black mottled, red mottled, pyle, partridge, silver duckwing, gold duckwing and exchequer.

Irrespective of plumage colouring, all Leghorns should have

Good Leghorn legs should be a pronounced yellow and be well-rounded – flat-fronted shins should be avoided

a yellow or horn-coloured beak and red eyes. The face and wattles must be bright red, the ear lobes pure white (can be creamy), and the legs yellow/orange and featherless.

Both large fowl and bantam versions are available, with the latter being created during the 1920s. Today, American and continental Leghorns are bred to a completely different breed standard to the one approved by the Poultry Club here in the UK.

Male leghorn combs need to be bright red, evenly serrated, free from side sprigs and upstanding

Generally, the 'foreign' versions are smaller, with smaller combs but larger tails. Of the standardised colours in the UK, the red mottled represents the newest addition, and is the first new one to be approved for 20 years.

Nowadays it's probably the brown that is the most popular enthusiasts' bird among the large fowl, while the blacks and whites are favoured most strongly by bantam keepers. Within the Leghorn Club, the popularity of bantams outweighs that of the large fowl, but there's a general perception among enthusiasts that the large fowl is the more preferable as it's considered the better layer. In practical terms, though, it's the bantam which is often superior in this respect to many of the large fowl varieties currently available. Also, while you can expect a 2oz egg from a healthy large fowl hen, those from an equivalent bantam are only ½oz lighter.

What do you want?

The large fowl are quite difficult to buy nowadays; the number of breeders producing quality stock is relatively limited. The Leghorn Club is obviously the place to begin your search but, before starting, it's

Male tails should feature two pronounced and wide sickle feathers, plus additional furnishings

Red in the earlobes is always something to avoid if you have any aspirations in the show pen

This hen shows a poor, thin and creased ear lobe, plus a double-folded comb

important to decide whether you require birds for laying or exhibition purposes – there's an important distinction between the two. There remain a few decent laying strains here in the UK, from which keepers can expect 260 eggs a season.

Colour seems to make a big difference with regard to egg production. Exhibition-type whites might only lay 130 eggs. But blacks and some of the 'lesser' colours – including the exchequer – perform much better, producing perhaps 200 eggs a year. The way that the Fancy developed the breed for exhibition purposes over the years certainly had a detrimental effect on laying ability. For example, today's black and white birds are significantly larger than the original commercial Leghorn, and this is just one aspect that's affected their performance. Some of the newer colour varieties still benefit from the additional vigour introduced by the crossing process that created them, and this can certainly help with overall egg numbers.

While there is no recognised utility bantam strain of Leghorn currently available, we understand that a number of breeders are working towards this goal and these, once ready, will certainly offer an interesting and viable option for keepers interested in minimal feed input for maximum egg output.

The Leghorn is certainly a hardy breed which can be run outside quite happily under most conditions. The only time that keepers need to be wary is during periods of cold weather. Male blacks, whites and blues with the largest combs can be prone to frostbite damage (typically causing blackening of the comb tips) if exposed to really low temperatures and/or cold winds. Another danger is that male birds with very long wattles will get these wet when drinking, which can induce similar problems. There have also been stories of males getting their wattles stuck to frozen drinkers – another outcome to be avoided. Problems like these can be guarded against by smearing the headgear with a layer of Vaseline or lanolin.

Colour wars

The Leghorn doesn't eat excessively and will certainly happily supplement its feed ration with insects if given the opportunity to free-range. However, one important point to note is that it's never usually a good idea to run a flock of mixed colour Leghorns. They

An exchequer's wing must show almost equal amounts of black and white. Some have far too much white

Evenness of primary feather width is an important point to look out for – here it's not particularly good, and this can be a sign of inbreeding

tend to be quite picky with each other and, for this reason, are best kept in separate, colour-specific groups. So if you're starting with the breed, don't imagine you can simply go out and buy five different colours to look pretty in the garden, because there's likely to be trouble. Interestingly though, it seems that Leghorns are happy enough to run in a mixed breed flock, and aren't known for any aggression towards other birds under normal conditions.

Another key factor to bear in mind is that the Leghorn, with its Mediterranean temperament, is essentially a flighty and reasonably highly-strung bird. They are good fliers (bantams more so than large fowl) and will certainly require good, high fencing to prevent them from straying into neighbouring gardens or nearby trees. Some colours, such as buffs and blues, are more inclined to this behaviour than the rest. By and large though, the Leghorn isn't an outwardly aggressive breed. There will be the odd strain which might prove a little 'sparky' but in the main – assuming a reasonable level of regular handling and good welfare – these birds are great to live with and well-

A very proud-looking buff Leghorn male

suited to the family environment.

As far as feeding is concerned, the regime needed is somewhat dependant on the way in which the birds are kept. Given access to a free-range lifestyle, Leghorn hens can do perfectly as well on a wheat diet, supplemented with natural scratch feed, as they will on a formulated layers pellet. Those kept in closer confinement, however, will do best on layers pellets and will certainly require a constant supply of grit to aid shell formation.

With regard to parasites, there seems to be a strange tendency for mites and fleas to affect some colours of Leghorn much more than others. The exchequer, for example, rarely suffers with any sort of parasitic infestation, whereas whites can be especially prone to this sort of problem. The reasons for this aren't particularly clear, although it's been suggested that feather type and vigour are relevant factors, and also that this tendency can vary from strain to strain. Types with softer, silkier feathers seem to suffer more than the rest.

Natural approach

The Leghorn hen isn't widely regarded as a sitter but, if you're keen on the natural brooding approach then certainly don't write it off. Some hens will make perfectly good and reliable mothers but, once again, this tendency seems to be dependant on colour, with the buff probably being the most likely to be a broody.

If you're interested in exhibiting Leghorns it's worth noting that you can differentiate fairly quickly between good and bad examples when the birds are young. A poor comb, for example, can usually be identified after as little as three weeks, and the chicks can usually be sexed by this age too.

The ease of breeding varies across the colour range, with the white probably posing the greatest potential problems due mainly to the amount of inbreeding that's gone on over the years. As a general rule, large fowl tend to be less fertile than bantams, especially in the case of blacks and whites. Large fowl can also be more prone to physical defects such as twisted toes and other leg problems, which don't typically affect the bantams nearly as much. This can be a consequence of confinement, and it's important to note that the large fowl do require a reasonable amount of exercise to stay fit. It's also important that they're not 'forced' too much in the early stages. If they are under a heat lamp this needs to be carefully so that they're not 'drawnup'. Feed should be available constantly to ensure they don't outgrow their own strength.

Young black female

Lincolnshire Buff

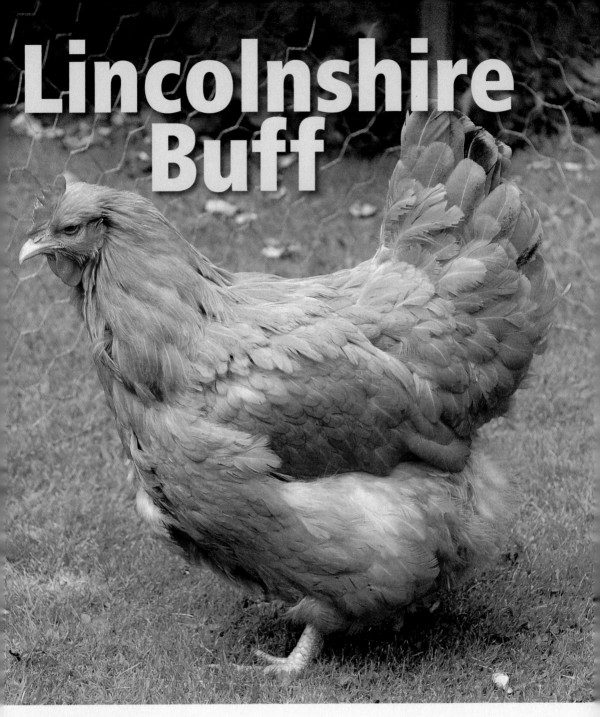

It's not an easy bird to source, but the Lincolnshire Buff is certainly worth the wait

Back in the 1850s, the colour buff really was the height of fashion. It was the colour of choice for smart young things; gentlemen favoured buff waistcoats and it was popular for ladies' dresses. Much of this trend seems to have been fuelled by the arrival of exotic Cochin fowl from China. It's hard to appreciate nowadays just what an effect these large, fancy new birds had upon their introduction but, by all accounts, they caused little short of a sensation across the land.

The buff Cochins were used extensively as crosses with both the four-toed farmyard fowl, and the popular five-toed, rich brown and red birds from Sussex, Kent and Surrey, to produce hardy and very useful offspring with a wonderful mixture of attractive colouring.

One particular cross – between the

AT A GLANCE

Size
Heavy large fowl

Origin
Great Britain

Weights
Male - 4-5kg (9-11lbs)
Female – 3.1-4kg (7-9lbs)

Egg laying
160+ pa

Colours
Buff (mixture of orange, copper, chestnut and ginger buff)

Cochin and Dorking, made in the East of England during the mid-1850s – is thought to have produced the basis of a breed that became known as the Lincolnshire Buff. As Harrison Weir noted in his excellent *Our Poultry*: 'This was the commencement of this particular cross in Lincolnshire, and finding that they were hardy, easily reared, quick in growth and readily fattened, they gradually grew in the estimation of farmers and others; and so plentiful did they at last become, that after some few years they were known in the London and other markets as Lincolnshire Buffs.'

Achieving a well-positioned fifth toe remains difficult. A clear separation between it and the fourth one is required, but is tricky to get in practice. Pink scale colouring on this male's leg is acceptable when in breeding condition

A Eye should be orange. Avoid pale eyes, although this does happen to an extent as a bird ages.

B Medium-sized single, upright comb should top a strong male head. It needs to be free from side sprigs, smooth, finely-textured and, ideally, feature five or six evenly-spaced spikes. This male's comb isn't ideal. Comb can flop over on pullets, but will often straighten with age.

C Beak should be white or horn coloured, and stout. Deformities, such as twisted or crossed beaks, are rare.

D Wattles need to be of medium size, rounded and finely textured. Face should be red and smooth too.

E A good Lincolnshire Buff will display an alert, upright and bold appearance. Its body should be large, deep and moderately long, with a broad breast and well-rounded keel bone. Bird should feel heavy and solid when handled.

F Wings are moderately large and should feature attractive copper colouring on the bow coverts. Body feathering generally is a pleasant mixture of orange, copper, umber and ginger buff. Ideally, the neck and saddle hackle feathers should show the same shade of rich orange.

G Legs must be white – horn colouring on the front scales of males in breeding condition is acceptable – and free from feathering (it does occur). The feet must be the same colour, and feature five straight toes with white nails.

H The fifth toe should be above and quite separate from the fourth, pointing straight back and, ideally, curving upwards. Its absence represents a serious fault.

I Feathering should generally be close and broad. Watch out for too much fluffiness in this region, especially on the hens.

J Tail side hangers should be a rich copper or bronze colour, while the main tail feathers and sickles need to be the same, but shading into umber. Avoid birds showing black with any hint of a beetle green sheen. Also, watch out for white feathering in the wings or at the base of the tail on male birds; very difficult to breed out.

K Sickle feathers should be moderately long and well curved. Tail is of medium size and should be carried well out. Length of sickle is one of the few factors still lacking on today's bird compared to those in Harrison Weir's day.

J Back needs to be broad, featuring abundant saddle feathers of medium length.

No records

Unfortunately, Weir never got the chance to paint examples of the breed so there's no historical record of the original Lincolnshire Buff's colouring, and all we have as a clue to appearance are a couple of black-and white sketches that he made in the early 1890s.

Despite enjoying 40 or so years of steadily growing popularity and recognition, the Lincolnshire Buff was destined to remain a regional breed and, ultimately, even this status was snatched from its grasp. Having been created with the simple objectives of producing a practical utility bird in a popular colour, things progressed well enough until William Cook created the Buff Orpington in 1894 and a significant factor was that Cook managed to get his buff version standardised with the Poultry Club of Great Britain, so breeders and fanciers had an agreed format to aim at. The Lincolnshire Buff was never standardised, so there was little focus to its breeding.

Like for like?

In those days, of course, Cook's Orpington was a country mile away from the fluffy, 'feather-duster'-like fowl we have today, and presented a much more businesslike appearance; quite similar in many respects to the Lincolnshire Buff. But the popularity of the Lincolnshire Buff continued to fade as the century drew to a close and though it remained a reasonably popular meat bird and still a good layer, the breed's influence became centred on the Lincolnshire town of Horncastle, north of Boston, and by the 1920s the breed's time in the commercial spotlight had ended. Things then went very quiet indeed for the breed and, at some point during the following 60 years, it was lost altogether.

However, it's not all doom and gloom thanks, essentially, to the efforts of Lincolnshire-based poultry enthusiast Brian Sands. He began his determined efforts to re-create the breed in 1986, when he took over a cancelled development program

Combs should not be too large and as evenly serrated as possible. Some birds suffer with too great an area of unserrated comb at the front

Female headgear is smaller, as you'd expect. Wattles are much neater, but still finely textured

that had been running at Riseholme Agricultural College. There wasn't a lot to work with, though. All he was able to rescue from the college was one young cockerel and four hens and among his new acquisitions he found feathered legs and four-toed feet; both serious faults for a Lincolnshire Buff.

Also, with nothing more than written accounts regarding plumage colouring to refer to, Brian had to set about the re-

creation job using little more than gut instincts. One of his first thoughts was that he wanted to create a visual distinction between the new Lincolnshire Buff and other buff-coloured breeds. He was also keen to establish a consistency among the birds being bred, believing that in the past there had been too much tolerance of feather colour discrepancy.

So, with the careful introduction of fresh buff Cochin and red Dorking blood, he opted to select for a more natural type of colouring, allowing the male birds in particular to show darker feathering on the neck, wings and tail. He was after an attractive medley of orange, chestnut, copper and buff, along the lines of that found on the Nankin bantam. He established his own written standard for the breed then, with the help of Peter Hadgraft, set about trying to get this approved and accepted by the Poultry Club of Great Britain. This finally happened in 1998, following the formation of the Lincolshire Buff Poultry Society in 1995.

Rare breed

Despite all Brian's work, and the sterling efforts of the other stalwarts in the Lincolnshire Buff Society over the past ten years, the breed remains a rarity today and breeder shortage means that buying Lincolnshire Buffs is no easy job. It's certainly not a breed you can expect to buy 'off the shelf', and anyone interested must be prepared for – and accept – a lengthy wait.

Those lucky enough to get hold of good examples of this breed will be rewarded with birds that are a joy to keep. The Lincolnshire Buff hen is a hardy yet docile chicken, with a pleasant, calm nature and an innate contentedness that'll see it scratch happily in a garden pen with the lowest of fencing surrounds. But they love to free-range too. Male birds are generally placid too, although some have been known occasionally to show a feisty side, both to fellow flock members and their owners!

The straightforward, no-

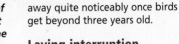

A degree of umber (not black) in the main wing feathers, as on this male, is desirable. You'll typically find less – or none at all – on a female

away quite noticeably once birds get beyond three years old.

Laying interruption

The hens are certainly known for their broodiness and make fantastic, reliable sitters. They're good, attentive mothers as well, although some keepers do mention that the tendency to go broody does interfere with egg production if it's not carefully controlled. With this in mind, keepers can expect 160+ eggs from a young, healthy hen. It's also worth noting that the breed's table qualities remain and, for keepers so inclined, a large cock bird will make an extremely tasty and satisfying roast.

In reality, of course, with so few people breeding Lincolnshire Buffs at the moment, sourcing birds

nonsense nature of the breed means that these birds are easy and undemanding to look after. They tend to be tough too, and show no characteristic susceptibility to any of the common poultry-related diseases. In fact, they seem remarkably resistant to respiratory problems when compared to many other pure breeds. Breeding shouldn't throw up any serious problems either. Fertility levels are generally good and chicks typically hatch well and grow strongly. It's worth noting, though, that most male birds tend to be more vigorous early in the year, and that age can be a significant factor too. Breeders do report that fertility levels fall

The Lincolnshire Buff produces good-sized, tinted eggs, and you can expect 160+ from a healthy young hen

Good undercolour right down to the skin is another important requirement. Any grey colouring here is an undesirable defect

through the Society really is the only option, which means you will certainly be getting well-bred birds.

This breed is definitely one that's thoroughly deserving of greater support, not only because it remains such a rarity, but also thanks to the fact that it offers a genuinely practical option for keepers wanting a straightforward, useful performer. The feathering – while not conventionally 'buff' – is undeniably attractive and, in itself, should endear the breed to many potential owners.

White in the tail feathers, at the base of the tail or in the wings is a serious fault to be avoided. Also steer clear of birds showing any beetle-green sheen on black feathering, as this example does

YES OR NO?

✔ Attractive mellow colouring.
✔ Easy to keep.
✔ Placid non-flyer.

✘ Very limited stocks.

Marans

This utility bird from France offers
something for everyone

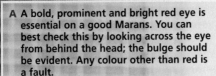

A **A** bold, prominent and bright red eye is essential on a good Marans. You can best check this by looking across the eye from behind the head; the bulge should be evident. Any colour other than red is a fault.

B **B** The comb should be single, upright and bright red. A maximum of seven points is the ideal, and the texture should be fine on all headgear. Avoid folded combs, and those showing side sprigs. Any white in the ear lobe is a serious fault, and should definitely be avoided. Birds with this shouldn't be used for breeding if you have ambitions in the show pen. However, this isn't an issue that affects overall laying ability.

C **C** The Marans's beak should be short, broad and horn-coloured on the female. Male examples should show a white beak.

D **D** A wide and deep chest (from its utility roots) is another Marans characteristic. The keel (breast bone) is very long too, extending well back underneath, between the hocks. This should be as straight as possible.

E **E** Feathering should be reasonably tight all over. Some white undercolour is acceptable on male cuckoos, but avoid too much – especially in young birds. The best birds will show cuckoo patterning right down to the skin.

F **F** There should be four, well-spread and straight toes on each foot. Avoid duck-footed examples (when the rear toe lies close to the ground).

G **G** Shanks must be featherless and white on both males and females. However, it's quite normal for first-year females to have quite dark shanks. This blackish pigmentation should disappear a few weeks after the hen comes into lay. Similar discolouration on male legs should be avoided.

H **H** Avoid thighs that are too long in relation to the shank; the Marans should never appear too tall and gangly. Thighs should be well-fleshed and set widely apart.

I **I** The tail should be carried high on both male and female birds. Some white in the sickle feathers on male birds does occur, but isn't a serious fault. Occasional gold feathers can appear on males among the sickles or neck hackle feathers. The odd one is fine (tends to result in a better colour sheen on the females!), but more than this is a problem.

J **J** A Maran's back and abdomen should be broad and, overall, the bird should have a solid feel about it when handled, indicating good meat potential.

The attractive copper black is one of the most popular French Marans; note the feathered legs on this male

The Marans, as we know it, is a comparatively new breed. It arrived here from its native France during the late 1920s, when 60 hatching eggs were imported by Mr JS Parkin, manager at Stanbridge Earl Poultry Farm in Kent (then owned by Lord Greenaway). Straightforward utility breeds were all the rage between the wars, and the Marans joined a group of useful, practical breeds that included the Barnevelder and Welsummer, which arrived in the UK from continental Europe.

Parkin's eggs hatched to produce a range of colours. In France at that time, the Marans was very much a regional farmyard fowl. It had been developed in an area about halfway down the west coast, and took its name from a town just north-east of the port of La Rochelle. Enjoying a reputation as a hardy, no-nonsense breed, the Marans got on with its typically active life, producing plenty of eggs and being good for the table when needed.

Mixed bag

The originals were smaller than the birds we have now, and had feathered legs too. The story goes that Parkin's eggs produced a collection of cuckoo, white, black and gold cuckoo examples, and that all layed copious numbers of a wonderfully dark, chocolate-coloured eggs; still something of a novelty at that time.

But Parkin and his associates – including William Powell-Owen, the notable utility breeder and author – wasted little time in refining the breed, selecting and breeding for what they considered to be its best points. One of the primary objectives appears to have been the removal of the leg feathering, to avoid unwanted similarity with the North Holland Blue, another cuckoo-coloured, feather-legged breed. They succeeded with this aim and, nowadays, feathering on a Marans' legs is a serious fault for birds being bred to the breed standard.

The result of Parkin's careful breeding work was the

This dark cuckoo Marans female in the main picture shows good type (the apparent 'lump' in her back is simply ruffled feathers)

Poultry Club-approved standardisation for dark, silver and gold cuckoo versions, plus black. The original white fell by the wayside early on and, today, blacks plus the silver and golden cuckoo versions are extremely rare. In real terms, enthusiasts now are left with the dark cuckoo as the only practical option existing in workable numbers.

The Marans caught on pretty quickly here after its introduction. In those days, eggs with dark, chocolate-coloured shells were the big attraction, and the breed soon built a reputation around this desirable characteristic. However, its popularity was destined ultimately to remain strongest among backyard keepers. The onset of the Second World War, followed by the 'hybridisation' of commercial poultry during the post-war era, spelt the end of any serious farming interest in breeds such as this one. While the Marans' dual-purpose attributes proved very attractive to the small-scale and enthusiast keeper, they weren't suited to those involved in the new, intensive approaches to egg and meat production.

French following

The Marans Club was formed in the 1950s, and continues to flourish today. This enthusiastic organisation caters for the feather-legged French version too, even though these types are not yet standardised in the UK. Their popularity is growing steadily here, with the two favourite colour varieties being the copper black and the wheaten. The French birds are smaller overall but they lay just as well as the English variety and, although the eggs are more rounded, they normally boast an even richer chocolate brown shell.

A bantam version was created in the UK during the 1950s although, in those days, it wasn't laying the characteristic dark egg... in fact, the shell was white! This problem had been caused by the out-crossing needed to get the bird down to the appropriate bantam size. It wasn't until the early 1970s that Andy Marshall and Ken Bosley set to work putting this right.

Ken had a large fowl Marans that accidentally mated with an Old English Game on his farm. The

A proud cuckoo Marans male, displaying desirable white legs and beak. Some white in the tail like this is perfectly acceptable

offspring were mated with a small, prize-winning Marans large fowl cockerel, and there followed a five-year breeding program in which Andy and Ken carried out two hatchings a year and selected purely for egg colour and breed conformation. The result was a dark-egg laying dark cuckoo Marans bantam.

Getting hold of good Marans is reasonably easy, as long as you work with the breed club. Seeking out birds on the open market is much more risky, and can be fraught with problems. The fact that the cuckoo markings are a dominant characteristic means that it's relatively easy to breed

AT A GLANCE

Size
Large, heavy; soft feather

Origin
France

Weights
Large male – 3.6kgs (8lbs)
Large female – 3.2kgs (7lbs)

Bantam male – 910g (32oz)
Bantam female – 790g (28oz)

Egg laying
220+ pa

Colours
Black, dark cuckoo, golden cuckoo, silver cuckoo

Assessing a Marans is all about feel. The quality of a good bird is gauged by its fullness of breast, width of back and abdomen plus its general solidity

examples that *look* OK, but which fail completely to produce the desirable dark-shelled eggs. These 'less accomplished' birds can be sold as the genuine article, and the inexperienced owner remains none the wiser until the hens come into lay and plain, tinted eggs start being produced.

But bag yourself some good birds from a top utility strain supplied by a recognised breeder and you won't look back. Marans are a really honest breed; they simply deliver the goods! There really are very few downsides to their ownership. Like other breeds that have their roots set in the farmyard, these birds are extremely hardy, active and love to free-range.

Good looking

Marans are attractive chickens, with a broad, deep and well-fleshed body. The head sits on top of a medium- length neck, and should feature large, prominent red eyes, a single, upright comb (with up to seven serrations) and a medium-sized, light-coloured beak. The cuckoo varieties are certainly interesting and attractive to look at, featuring an allover cuckoo pattern with each feather being banded with light and dark to create a pleasing overall effect.

As far as general character is concerned, the Marans can be a bit of a 'mixed bag'. Much, it seems, depends on the strain and the way the birds have been reared. Females are generally docile, but the males can become a little feisty and protective of their hens during the breeding season. This is something to watch for, especially if the birds are confined in a smallish area. However, be aware that you can stir-up trouble if you try to introduce Marans to new birds; they will sometimes develop into bullies if this happens. However, they will happily live alongside different breeds if all have grown up together. Generally, though,

Don't worry too much about pigmentation on the legs of young hens. This should disappear when laying begins

Watch out for leg feathering like this; not a good sign

these are busy birds that love to keep active. They're great to have around the garden, and will happily pick away at slugs, snails and other gardening pests.

When buying, one of the best ways to assess breeding stock is by careful handling. Experienced keepers advocate doing this in the dark, so all your senses focus on how the bird's body feels, rather than being distracted by its appearance. In the show pen a whopping 60% of the total points available is awarded for the bird's type, carriage, table merits, size and quality. Colour and marking only account for 15% of the points.

So, what you're after is a bird with a solid, deep body, a broad chest and plenty of width across the abdomen and back. Combining these characteristics will result in the delivery of plenty of meat and a good level of egg production. The cost of buying Marans can vary enormously, depending on where and what you buy. But, as a guide, you should expect to pay £20-30 per bird for good, large fowl stock *(2009 prices)*. Bantams are a little cheaper, at £15-25 for similar quality birds.

As you might have guessed, the Marans' real *forté* is its utility performance. It's a hard breed to show outside the club's own classes and it rarely scoops any sort of overall award, such as Best in Show. It's not really a fashionable bird in that respect, unlike the Australorp, Cochin, Sebright or Wyandotte for example. But they can offer an excellent and potentially very successful way into the egg showing arena.

Breeding potential?

Generally the Marans is a good bird to breed with. Fertility tends to be excellent if you're working with a good strain. However, it's worth noting that the nature of the egg – it has a thicker shell than most others – means that the internal membrane can present a significant barrier to the emerging chick if humidity levels are wrong during the latter stages of hatching. So, if you're using an incubator, especially a 'still air' machine (no fan), you need to be very careful at this stage. Get it wrong and the levels of dead-in-shell could be high.

When handling birds to buy, check that the breast bone extends right back to between the hocks

Cuckoo patterning that extends down to the skin is a sign of a good utility Marans. Watch for too much white in the undercolour

A good wing without too much white

Key points to look for on the female Marans head include horn-coloured beak, smooth textured comb, wattles and ear lobes plus a bright and prominent red eye

This is the primary reason that most enthusiasts keep Marans. Eggs from French Marans (on the left) tend to be more rounded and not as 'traditional' egg-shaped as those from the British variety. Healthy young hens of both types, though, should produce well over 200 eggs a season

If the humidity levels are too low then the membrane will become too tough for the chick to break through; if it's too high then the developing chick will absorb too much water and won't be able to turn inside the shell because it has become physically too large to do so. Naturally incubated eggs – the Marans hen is a great and reliable sitter – are normally fine. Chicks that do hatch will be strong and rapid growers, and they're also quick to feather.

An added advantage, when breeding cuckoo Marans, is that the chicks display elements of sex linkage from an early age; there are significant differences which can be used to tell male from female. After as little as three weeks, the comb on male birds is clearly visible, and the plumage is obviously lighter than that on the female. Pullets are significantly darker at this age, and tend to have longer tails as well.

The French versions grow even faster and are precocious too; males can be crowing after just 14 weeks. They grow into smaller birds, ultimately, but usually tend to retain more of the breed's traditional utility characteristics than the English version.

The strength and general hardiness of the Marans means that it's very resistant to all the common poultry ailments. Marek's simply isn't an issue. The breed continues to benefit from a broad genetic base in the UK, which undoubtedly helps when it comes to health and strength issues. There's very little in-breeding going on, so serious disease-related problems are rare.

At a practical, backyard level, you'll need a decent fence to keep Marans where you want them, unless you opt to clip a wing or two. Being a heavy breed, they're not naturally flighty, but some strains can be more feisty than others. Much also depends on how the birds have been reared but, even with the most wayward characters, nothing higher than a six-foot fence should be necessary. Large fowl Marans that have enjoyed plenty of handling all their lives should be perfectly well contained by fencing that's four feet high. Bantams, being smaller and lighter, might present more of a containment challenge!

A three-day-old copper black Marans chick

YES OR NO?

✔ Very hardy.
✔ Dark eggshell colour.
✔ Superb layer.
✔ Disease resistant.
✔ Simple to keep.
✔ Good table bird.

✗ 'Fakes' around.
✗ Males can be protective.

Minorca

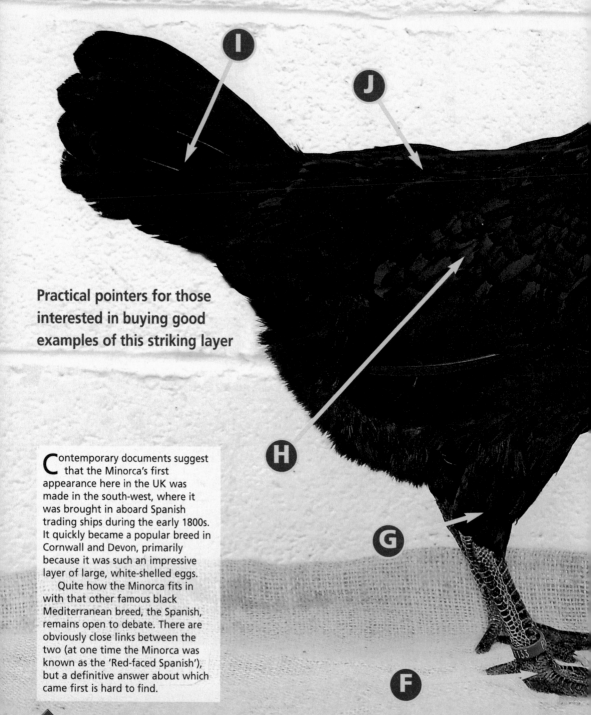

Practical pointers for those interested in buying good examples of this striking layer

Contemporary documents suggest that the Minorca's first appearance here in the UK was made in the south-west, where it was brought in aboard Spanish trading ships during the early 1800s. It quickly became a popular breed in Cornwall and Devon, primarily because it was such an impressive layer of large, white-shelled eggs.

Quite how the Minorca fits in with that other famous black Mediterranean breed, the Spanish, remains open to debate. There are obviously close links between the two (at one time the Minorca was known as the 'Red-faced Spanish'), but a definitive answer about which came first is hard to find.

A The eye should be full, expressive and as dark as possible (brown). Red eyes represent a serious exhibition fault.

B The male comb should be erect while the female's lies folded, as here. Ideally the depth of the serrations should extend to half that of the whole comb, but you will find huge variations. There should be four or five serrations, and the male's comb should also follow the neck line at the rear; it shouldn't ride off the back of the head. The number of folds in the female comb is an important exhibition issue, and a source of confusion. A single fold is the ideal, where the comb rises up from the head, leans one way and then folds back the other. But this is often confused with a 'double-folded' comb.

C Beak should be moderately long, but stout, and very dark in colour.

D Wattles should be long and pendulous (hanging slightly below the ear lobes) and showing as few folds as possible.

E Breast should be full and round. Feathering is all fairly tight, even though the breed is classed as a 'soft feather'. Colour of feather should be strong right down to the skin. White feathers (or patches on wing feathers) in black adults are a major fault, although don't be too alarmed if you spot the odd white one in a young bird; it'll probably moult out.

F Four toes on each foot.

G Legs should be dark slate on black birds (slate blue on blues and pink on whites). They do lighten with age, but should be as dark as possible on young birds. Avoid short legged versions, but also 'stiltiness'.

H Wings are medium in size but should be carried fairly high, and tight to the body.

I Tail should be carried relatively low, to enhance the length of back. In exhibition females the tail should be 'whipped' (showing a slight curve at the tip).

J Back should be long and as flat as possible.

K Ear lobe should be large (not exceeding 2.75in in depth on a large fowl), Valencia almond-shaped and show good thickness. Paper-thin lobes, which curl and 'dish' as a result, are to be avoided. They must be pure white – black and red blotchiness can appear. Red on the back of the lobe is perfectly acceptable. Watch for, and avoid, twisted lobes.

A Minorca's face should be a good, solid, deep red colour. Watch out for signs of white, though – it's a serious fault that can result when birds are bred for exaggerated ear lobe size. Some facial whiteness can appear on older birds as a natural consequence of ageing

The Minorca's popularity wasn't confined to the south-west of England, however, and it wasn't long before its laying abilities had come to the attention of poultry keepers across the land. It developed a strong following in London where many owners kept the birds successfully in a 'back yard', urban environment. Such was the success of the breed that, during its heyday in the early 1900s, there were no fewer than six specialist clubs for the Minorca in the UK – one of which was based in London.

Unfortunately, like so many other traditional utility breeds, the Minorca's spell of laying dominance and general popularity came to rather an abrupt end with the post-war arrival of the modern hybrid birds from America. Although the Minorca was capable of producing an impressive 200 large eggs a season, the hybrids were laying 300 in the same period, and eating less food into the bargain; in purely commercial terms, there was no contest.

Limited choice

There are three colours of Minorca accepted in the UK, as described in the Poultry Club breed standards; black, blue and white. Other options are available abroad – Germany and America – where it's possible to find buff and cuckoo as well (neither are accepted here).

The white and the blue are both currently extremely rare here in the UK, and it's the black which dominates now in terms of numbers. Consequently, it's this type that we're featuring here. It's not totally clear why the colour balance has veered so much in favour of the black, although one simple explanation may be that, with its large white ear lobe, large bright red comb and pure black plumage, the black version presents the most strikingly attractive combination.

From a buying point of view, the Minorca is currently a reasonably easy bird to buy, assuming you work through the breed club. Currently this organisation has about 120 members, although it's probably fair to say that only about 40 of these breed in large enough numbers to have enough birds to sell on. The majority of club members only keep a handful of birds, and breed just enough to replenish their own flocks. However, there are suppliers enough dotted around the country to ensure that most people interested should be able to find good quality stock without having to travel too far.

Chicken breeds from the Mediterranean generally have a bit of a reputation for being excitable and 'flighty'. In the case of the Minorca, though, this is very controllable, especially with adequate care and attention early on. In common with most other light breeds, young Minorcas can be a bit of a handful, but things normally calm down once the birds reach maturity, at about the five-month mark. Much also depends on

The female comb won't always fold as it should and, while this is irrelevant for the backyard keeper, it will seriously hinder a hen's chances in the show pen

While some may consider the above hen to have a double-folded comb it is, in fact, the correct, single-folded type. The comb leaves the head, veers right and then folds back across the top, which helps ensure that it sits well. Breeding good males from folded-comb females can be tricky, as the comb can be inclined to fold too, which is not what you want in a male.

Traditionally, show breeders would run two breeding pens, one with females featuring short, upright combs, to help with the production of good male headgear

Male Minorcas should always display an erect, single and well serrated comb. The comb, and the breed's large white ear lobes, are its crowning glories. Tails should never be held high

the amount of human contact the young birds receive. Frequent handling from the start will help enormously. Birds that are treated well, with plenty of human interaction, will grow up to become very approachable adults, that will be as calm and handlable as you like. They can certainly become very family-friendly birds; great for the garden and with children.

What's more, for a breed which originated in a hot climate, the Minorca is a surprisingly hardy bird. Like most other utility types, it was developed originally as a forager capable of living happily outside. Obviously, though, the strains here have acclimatised to the colder environment and now cope extremely well under all conditions, assuming adequate husbandry levels of course.

Just about the only climate-related factors which can still pose a problem are really cold, frosty weather, plus wind and rain. The large size of the Minorca's comb

(both on the males and females) means that frostbite is a potential risk. However, cases of this are relatively rare here, and it seems that temperatures need to drop below -5°C before trouble can strike. Most experienced keepers, if

they are worried, will add a smear of Vaseline to exposed combs for extra protection when absolutely necessary.

If the birds are kept dry and out of the wind in a well-made house with plenty of clean litter, then

Keep an eye out for white patches in the wing feathers; another feature to be avoided if possible

problems will be very rare indeed. It's also important to keep the birds out of wind and rain (as with any other breed). In the case of the Minorca, though, exposure to these conditions can promote the formation of blisters on the ear lobes. These will usually clear up naturally if the bird is protected from the worst of the weather, but a dab or two of zinc oxide cream will help speed the healing process.

Day to day

The Minorca is the largest of the light breeds, and so generally is able to hold its own with most other breeds. Consequently, if you're interested in running some in a mixed flock, this shouldn't be a problem. Likewise, these birds tend not to suffer with bullying.

From a keeping point of view, just about their only flaw is that the large fowl versions don't go broody, so natural incubation really isn't an option if you want to rear your own birds. Fortunately, all is not lost as the bantam version makes an excellent broody and attentive mother (presumably due to the inter-breed used to create it).

Up until about five years ago, bantam Minorcas outnumbered the large fowl equivalent by perhaps

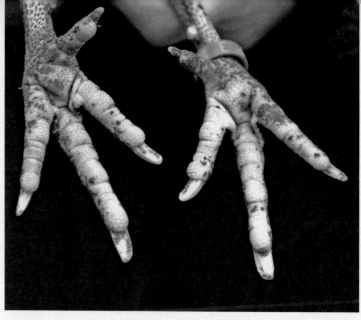

A lighter colouring (pink/cream) on the underside of the foot is perfectly acceptable

five-to-one. Today, the large have really caught up in popularity terms. Traditionally, bantams were the favoured show bird among exhibitors, but a recent increase in breed awareness among domestic enthusiasts new to the poultry keeping hobby has brought about a significant change. Nevertheless, bantams still represent a great

ownership option, especially if space is tight. They lay just about as well as the large fowl and, although the eggs are smaller, they're actually impressively large given the size of the birds.

Finally, it's worth noting that the Minorca's general hardiness ensures that it remains usefully resistant to most of the common poultry problems and diseases. These birds are strong and durable if looked after correctly, and shouldn't suffer with any of the recognised nasties any more readily than other popular breeds.

Just about the only condition that some suffer with is 'twisted toe', although it appears that this isn't usually a genetic problem. There seems to be a link between this unfortunate condition and the use of infrared heat lamps during early rearing. Those breeders who use 'dull emitter'-type heat sources in the brooder rarely have problems, while those who choose an IR heat source sometimes do.

So, all in all, the Minorca represents a pretty good bet for any would-be keeper looking for a breed with striking appearance combined with good temperament and a genuinely practical laying ability.

So what are you waiting for? Get in touch with the club and track-down some top-quality examples today!

Black feathers should feature a beetle-green sheen, which is especially obvious in sunshine. Sometimes, however, it can appear blue instead of green, which is a fault if you are thinking of showing

Modern Game

This stunningly individual British breed has more to it than eye-catching looks

A Eyes should be prominent and bright, enhancing the birds active, alert manner. The colour varies from bright red to black. Avoid those with light eyes

B The Modern Game's beak should be long, gracefully-curved and thick-set and strong at the base. Colour varies depending on plumage; it should be willow on black-reds like this male, black on birchens, yellow on piles and whites.

C Neck on both large and bantam Modern Game should be long and slightly arched, contributing to the generally 'reachy' appearance of the bird.

D Modern Game should be wide and muscular at the front, with prominent shoulders. Check that the breast bone is straight all the way down; twisting or crookedness here is a serious fault.

E Wings are short and strong, and held tight to the body. Bantam versions are better fliers than the large, and are quite capable of getting up into nearby trees given the opportunity.

F Thighs should be long, muscular and powerful, with tight, short feathering.

G Leg colour should match that of the beak, and varies in the same way according to feather pattern. Refer to 'B' above. Check that the fronts of the legs are rounded; flat shins are most undesirable, as are short legs.

H Foot colour should match legs, and the four toes should be straight and well-spaced. Crooked toes, or a tendency towards duck-footedness and both defects to be avoided. Toe-nail colour should match that of the toes and legs.

I Tail should be short, fine and closely whipped together. Ideally it'll be carried slighty above the level of the body.

J On male birds, the sickle feathers should be narrow, well-pointed and only slightly curved. Walk away from birds displaying a squirrel or wry tail.

K A short, flat back is another Modern Game characteristic to look out for. Check carefully for any crookedness and leave birds showing this well alone.

Modern Game birds must surely rank among the most visually distinctive of breeds. Long legs and snake-like necks, combined with tight feathering and minimal tails create an appearance that, while maybe not to everyone's taste, is undeniably striking. This outwardly distinguished look shouldn't come as a complete surprise in this particular case, though, as the Modern Game is all about image. It's a breed that was consciously honed to perfection for the show pen, in complete contrast to its fearsome forbears that were developed every bit as carefully but, in their day, for the fighting pit.

This nation's association with Game birds goes back thousands of years. Roman literature documents the use of fowl for 'pleasure and diversion' and it's widely believed that the latter related to cock-fighting. This was an extremely popular activity right across society, with enormous amounts of money being bet on the outcomes of individual fights.

Change of direction
But the practice of cock-fighting was eventually outlawed by an Act of Parliament in 1849, which left countless keepers and breeders with nothing to do with their birds. Many opted to satisfy their competitive urges in the less violent environment of the show hall. As it happened, this coincided with a general groundswell in the popularity of poultry shows, so

AT A GLANCE
Size
Hard feather

Origin
Great Britain

Weights
Large male – 3.20-4.10kg (7-9lb)
Large female – 2.25-3.20kg (5-7lb)
Bantam male – 570-620g (20-22oz)
Bantam female – 450-510g(16-18oz)

Egg laying
100+ pa

Colours
Birchen, black-red, wheaten, blue red, crele, gold & blue duckwing, pile, wheaten, black, blue, white, blue-red, silver-blue, lemon-blue

the timing couldn't have been better. In fact, the 1850s really were boom years in this respect.

As the competition started to get more serious, many Game breeders started looking at the ways in which they could develop the appearance and type of their birds. Obviously, they could do little about the characteristic and traditional hard feathering (short and close-fitting), but they could certainly increase the overall size and shape. The most common breeding cross used to achieve this was with the Malay, which introduced a good deal more height and different tail characteristics too.

Striking pile bantam female with pure white thighs, wings and tail, plus good yellow legs and beak

This is a large wheaten female; very rare nowadays

A pair of birchen bantam; the one in the foreground has darker head feathers, which is considered a fault

short-lived. The two world wars seemed to hit the breed hard; perhaps it simply wasn't useful enough in austere times when stock had to work to earn its keep.

The large version was particularly badly affected and it's never truly recovered. While the bantam did rise again to become a showman's favourite for a second time – and remains so to this day – the large Modern Game continues to struggle. The formation of the Modern Game Club in 1947 was probably key to the survival of the large version, but even its best efforts haven't helped this fine bird re-capture its past glories.

Plenty of choice

Today, the Modern Game is available in 15 standardised colours, all of which are available in bantam form, although the choice is a good deal more limited if you want large fowl. Essentially, the large fowl choice at the moment is between black-red partridge, pile and duckwing.

Plumage colour is a very important factor with these birds, and the options available can be a little baffling to the beginner. Type (the overall shape of the bird) is another vital consideration with this breed. The Modern Game must be upstanding and active; presenting plenty of lift, as though stretching up to its full height. These are essential requirements from a showing point of view.

The body should be short with a flat back, with the whole thing resembling an old-fashioned flat iron when viewed from above – wide shoulders, tapering towards the tail. Both the wings and the tail should be short; the males having narrow, pointed and slightly curved sickle feathers.

This evolutionary process which transformed these birds – then known as Exhibition Modern Game – from burley bruisers into tall, sleek exhibition favourites took about 50 years. So, by the early 1900s the breed was extremely popular. The classes at the major shows were bursting with both large and bantam versions, and the best examples were changing hands for anything up to £100 (the equivalent of £3,000 today!). Sadly, though, this peak was relatively

The head is long and narrow with prominent eyes (varying from red to black), a small single comb, wattles and ear lobes, and a relatively long beak. The neck is long, slightly curved and covered with 'wiry', short feathering.

Standing on long legs, the Modern Game displays muscular thighs and rounded, featherless shanks. Each foot has four toes, and leg and foot colour include yellow, willow and black, according to overall colouring. The combs and

Undubbed and dubbed brown red males. The red face is considered a fault

This is a large, black-red female. The fluffiness around the vent area is perhaps more than you might usually expect, but is more prominent on this bird because she's in lay

Sleek birchen female bantam. Note the correct black legs, eye and beak matched to a dark (mulberry) face, comb and wattles

wattles can vary in colour too, from red to dark purple and black, once again depending on feather colour.

The midlands and the north of England remain the heartland for Modern Game. The majority of club members live in these regions. Bird theft remains a underlying issue for keepers of these birds, which is why many are reluctant to reveal home addresses. Some thefts of large Moderns are driven by the unfortunate and misguided idea that they can be used for fighting; this is simply no longer the case. Large black-red hens can give the impression of a fighting bird, but this is in looks only. Other birds get stolen simply for their value.

Leg colour varies dramatically according to plumage pattern. It's important that the match is a correct one

Regrettably, there will always be a black market for show-winning stock. Although 'backyard' examples can start at £10 each at present prices (2009), prices can rise to £300-500 for a top-quality trio.

Top colours

As with most breeds, there are a few Modern Game plumage colours which outstrip the rest in popularity terms. Pick of the bunch is the black-red (partridge version first, followed by wheaten), then comes the pile, the brown-red and the birchen. The other laced colours (silver and lemon blue) aren't as popular for some reason, nor are black or whites, both of the latter being rare these days.

At a practical level, Modern Game are reasonably hardy given the limitations of their tight feathering and lack of fluff. So while they won't be happy stuck

One other issue that needs mentioning is that of dubbing, which is the removal of a male bird's comb, wattles and ear lobes. This is a controversial issue which, like tail or ear docking on dogs, arouses passionate debate from both sides of the argument. Dubbing is a practice with its roots set in the cock-fighting era.

Legally speaking, if birds are to be dubbed it must be done when they are no older than 72 hours, and be carried out by a responsible person. After this time limit, a vet will carry out this procedure for genuine, welfare-related reasons (frost bite, injury etc).

Final thoughts

However, it's important not to let the dubbing issue put you off getting involved with the Modern Game. It only really becomes significant for those keepers in the upper echelons of the exhibition scene; for everyone else it's not something to worry about.

The large fowl versions are stunningly impressive, especially the males, although they can become a little feisty as they mature. At the other end of the scale, the bantams are a delight, both in terms of appearance and personality. You really couldn't wish for a happier, friendlier little bird and, with the range of colours available, there's something to suite even those with the most exotic tastes.

One thing's for certain, the Modern Game possesses the sort of looks that are simply guaranteed to ensure that it'll never be regarded as 'just another chicken'. It's hard to put a finger on the emotions that these birds can stir up; they exude a beguiling mix of primitive power and delicate sleekness. The Modern Game certainly offers unique and fascinating poultry-keeping possibilities. •

A black red bantam female. As you might expect, the miniatures fly better than the large versions

half way up a mountain in freezing temperatures, they will happily scratch around outside under more temperate conditions. Most keepers nowadays house their birds in arks or houses with covered runs.

Modern Game can be regarded as an easy breed to own, with no specialist dietary of health-related requirements. The close-feathering also means that they are not particularly susceptible to mites or lice, and this is not a breed that suffers characteristically with Marek's disease or coccidiosis.

Fertility and hatchability rates are typically good. Chicks grow very well and are easy to brood and rear. Moderns are not aggressive towards each other. Groups of males that have been reared together will be perfectly happy. Once separated, though, they can't go back together.

Somewhat surprisingly, the large Moderns make quite good utility birds, in terms of egg production,

and will lay right through the spring, summer and autumn months. Bantams tend to be more seasonal, but still lay well.

The Modern female does go broody but egg numbers in the bantam need to be limited due to the relatively small body size and tight feathering; she simply won't be able to keep more than about six adequately warm. They make very attentive and protective mothers as well.

Large Modern Game are surprisingly good layers. Bantam eggs (on left) are a good deal smaller, and not so numerous

New Hampshire Red

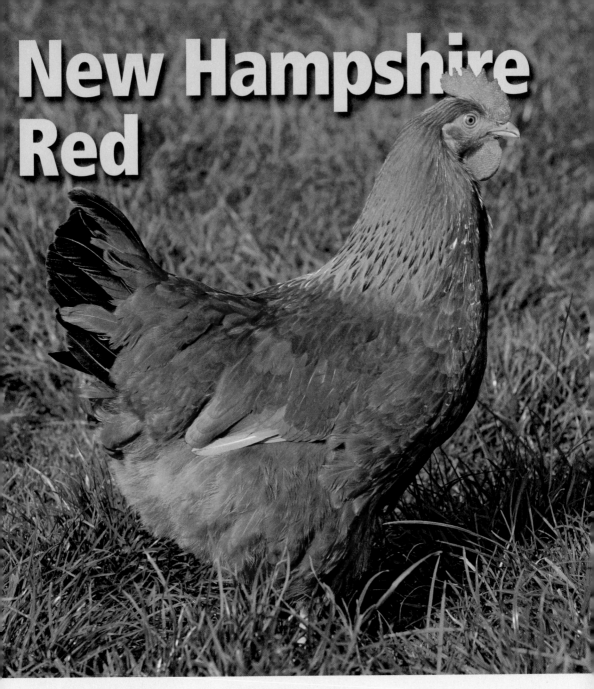

Above: New Hampshire Reds are rich in both colour and character; pleasant birds to look at, handle and live with

It's not often that you come across examples of 'keeping up with the Jones' in poultry breeding circles, but the New Hampshire Red seems to offer an element of exactly this sort of envy-led behaviour, albeit on a rather grand scale.

The New Hampshire Red was developed at the start of the 20th century as a dual-purpose breed directly from the Rhode Island Red. It appears that farmers in the state of New Hampshire wished to emulate their counterparts in nearby Rhode Island, by having their own distinct breed of chicken named after their state.

But they didn't set about the task with a complicated program of inter-breed crossing, they simply spent some 30 years refining the Rhode Island Red into a form that, while retaining all the most desirable utility characteristics, presented a significantly different plumage colour pattern.

Careful selection

In their lengthy quest for visual distinction, the breeders also took great care to select for key aspects such as fast feathering, rapid growth and overall vigour. It certainly proved to be a slow process which didn't really reach its conclusion until 1935, when the breed was officially recognised and became standardised in America. Following this formal acceptance, the first examples started trickling into the UK.

But despite its formidable laying performance – trials in America reportedly recorded one bird producing 332 eggs in a 52-week period – the NHR wasn't an immediate success in England; many believe that the breed was never able to escape the shadow of the more established and popular Rhode Island Red. Even despite the

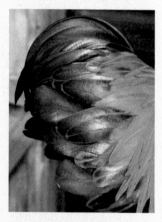

The male tail should show black main tail feathers, chestnut-edged black coverts and rich black sickle feathers. All black parts should display a lustrous green sheen

arrival of a bantam version – created during the 1980s – the New Hampshire Red continues to lack the support and popularity that its genuinely useful qualities surely deserve.

While the original creators of the breed never claimed it to be a great 'looker', the general feeling nowadays is that it's a good-looking and homely bird.

A Wattles on the male should be bright red (in common with the comb, face and ear lobes), smooth and not too large. Avoid those showing folds and wrinkles, which tends to be more common on large fowl than bantams. Ear lobes should be smooth and slightly elongated. Avoid birds showing any sign of white in the lobes.

B Beak must be medium length and strong and, according to the breed standard, reddish-brown in colour.

C Eye should be bright, prominent and bay-coloured; avoid those that appear pale. They are set high in the head.

D The comb should be single, of medium size, straight and, ideally, showing five, well-defined points. Side sprigs can be an issue so avoid birds showing this fault. Combs are obviously smaller on female birds, and can present a slight tilt at the rear, which is perfectly acceptable.

E Back should be medium length and broad down its length, displaying a gradual concave sweep to the tail.

F Male birds should display medium length, broad sickle feathers that extend beyond the main tail feathers, show a good curve and a beetle green sheen. Ideally the tail should be held at about 45°. Female NHRs typically hold their wellspread tails at a slightly lower 35° angle.

G Body should be stocky and thickset overall, with an almost cobby look to it. Feather structure is generally firm, with all fitting tightly to the body. Undercolour should be a light salmon colour, but this can turn a bit 'smoky' – not a really a serious exhibition defect.

H Wings are moderately large and should always be well folded and held tightly against the sides of the body. Ideally they should sit horizontally on male birds, but they can be slightly more angled on females. Watch for too much black in the wings, especially on male birds.

I Legs need to be strong and a rich yellow colour. The three toes at the front should be well-spread and straight, while the one at the rear should just touch the ground.

J Hackle feathers on New Hampshire Red males should be a solid, medium chestnut-red colour but on female birds these lower neck feathers are distinctly tipped with black.

K As you would expect for a bird offering good table qualities, the New Hampshire Red's breast should be deep, full, broad and well-rounded.

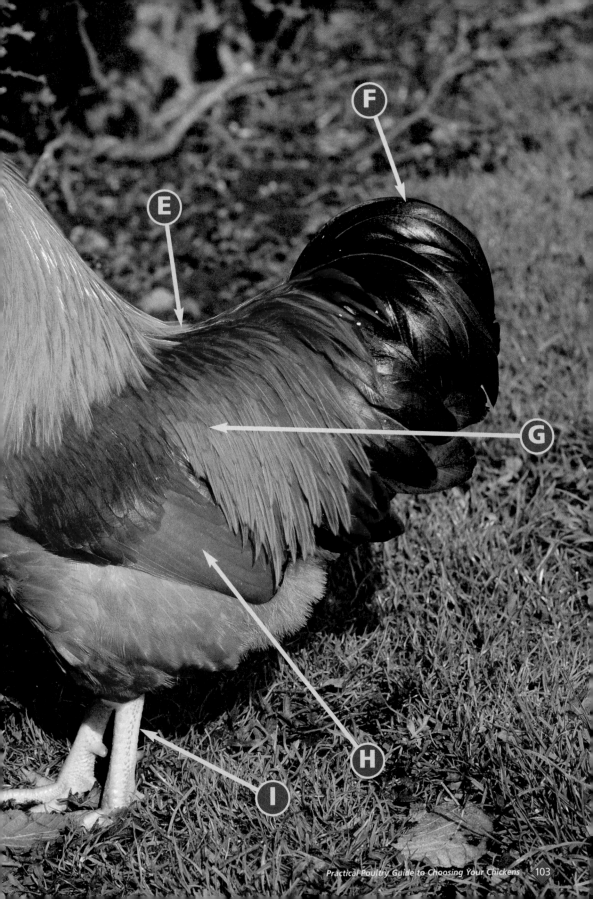

It presents a relatively broad, deep and well-rounded body that gives the breed a pleasantly attractive and traditional appearance. Its head, which tends to have a flatish top, features a proud single comb with five, well-defined points (larger in the centre than at the front or back). The eyes are large, prominent and set quite high in the head, and sit in a smoothskinned face above moderately long fold- and wrinkle-free wattles. The ear lobes form elongated ovals, lie close to the head and are smooth too.

The head tops-off a well-proportioned, medium-length and arched neck that's covered in flowing hackle feathers. This leads to a broad, medium-length back that forms a pleasingly sweeping, concave curve to the tail. Male birds have a more upright tail than the females, the breast is deep and well-rounded and the largish wings are held close to the body and horizontal, or as near to it as possible in the case of the females.

These birds sit on widely-spaced and strong legs that should be rich yellow in colour, with some red pigmentation down the outsides of the shanks and toes being desirable. Each foot should have four, well-spaced and straight toes.

Rich feathering

As far as feathering is concerned, the New Hampshire Red should present plumage showing a generally broad, firm structure, with feathers overlapping well and fitting tightly to the body. Colouring is a rich mixture of chestnut red, reddish-bay, red and

Watch out for too much black, in the form of peppering like this, on wing feathers

The breed standard calls for a light salmon-coloured undercolour but this can, as in this case, turn a little 'smoky' in places. This is not considered a defect

black, producing the overall look of what many regard as a really traditional and friendly, farmyard-type fowl.

This idea of friendliness is further enhanced by the breed's personality, which is generally docile and calm. Consequently, these birds – in either bantam or

Rich yellow legs and feet are a New Hampshire Red breed standard requirement. Reddish-horn tinging is permitted, as is a line of reddish pigmentation down the outside of the shank and toes.

It's worth remembering that foot and leg colour does vary; the colour will drain away towards the end of a long laying season

large fowl form – are ideally suited to the domestic garden environment.

New Hampshire Reds love to freerange given the option and, seeing as these birds aren't fliers (even the bantams won't bother to flutter more than a foot or two off the ground), containment is never going to be a great issue, even in the most urban of keeping environments. In practical terms, fences need be little more than three or four feet high for basic containment.

These birds are happy in confinement as well assuming, of course, that they aren't overcrowded. They are hardy too, and aren't known as characteristic sufferers with any of the most common poultry diseases. So if you run a clean and well-ordered poultry setup, with appropriate levels of husbandry, then the good news is that the New Hampshire Red represents one of the simplest and most straightforward keeping options around.

However, it's not all good news. One of the biggest struggles

Female (left) and male illustrate the difference in neck hackle feather colouring

anyone interested in the breed is likely to have relates to actually sourcing good examples in the first place. The relative scarcity of the New Hampshire Red means that tracking down worthwhile birds at the moment is likely to be a challenge. While trips to a few poultry sales and livestock auctions may well turn up a handful of examples, unless you're extremely lucky, birds found in this way will rarely live up to expectations.

Sourcing stock
The accepted way of finding good quality birds, whatever the breed, is to locate recommended breeders via the official breed club. It's only with this sort of word-of-mouth referral that you can proceed with

Bantams are more popular than the large fowl New Hampshire Reds these days, in common with many other breeds. Both versions can be equally productive with regard to egg numbers

some sort of confidence (and potential for comeback, should it be necessary) about the birds you're buying. Unfortunately, in this case, the New Hampshire Red Club is one of the smaller single breed clubs, with just 30 or so members. This means that both sale birds and the quality breeders producing them are bound to be in short supply. Patience is certainly a vital requirement if you're after good stock. Chris Woolley, whose prize-winning birds are featured in the photographs here, told me that it took him a whole year to find some large fowl examples that he was happy to buy.

This is a great shame because it's likely that this sort of limitation in supply, combined with lengthy waiting times, will put the majority of potential keepers off the breed at the first hurdle. With many newcomers to the hobby expecting to be able to buy the birds of their choice 'off the shelf', the kind of delay associated with the New Hampshire Red will surely dissuade most enquirers. It's a vicious circle really; the breed's relative rarity is one of the primary factors that's *keeping* it scarce.

There's no doubt that the New Hampshire Red has much to offer the domestic keeper, whatever their level of experience. Of course, as with so many other breeds, the strains available today don't perform nearly as well as their ancestors, in terms of laying ability. Nevertheless, a healthy young hen should still be capable of producing 170+, good-sized tinted eggs in a season, and the bantam versions are equally productive.

Poor sitters
Another widely-held belief, that you'll often find mentioned in poultry books, is that New Hampshire Red hens make good broody mothers. The reality, it seems, is rather different. Chatting to Chris Woolley while researching this feature, his experience suggests otherwise. As far as he, and other specialist breeders he knows are concerned, this just isn't the case nowadays. You simply can't depend on these hens to be reliable sitters, and anyone with aspirations as a breeder should choose to use an incubator.

This aside, however, the New Hampshire Red is a good breed to breed with. Fertility levels are generally high so hatch rates should be good, assuming all else is correct. The chicks are typically strong too, feathering-up quickly and growing strongly and fast right from the off. The youngsters are normally developed enough to be taken off heat by the six-week mark. What's more, the usually docile nature of this breed means that problems within the flock – bullying, feather pecking etc – should be rare, adding further to the appealing, ease-ofownership aspect.

There is no doubt that, assuming you can get hold of some stock, the New Hampshire Red represents a very smart choice for the keeper who seeks an interesting, attractive and worthwhile utility chicken. While its days of setting laying records are long gone, the production potential of hens from a good strain remains strong enough to meet the needs of the most demanding backyard pure-breed poultry keeper. But, perhaps more importantly, the breed itself is certainly worthy of a good deal more support. With the number of breeders currently at a worryingly low level, if ever a breed needed an influx of serious interest, this is it. •

YES OR NO?
✔ **Good temperament.**
✔ **Traditional looks.**
✔ **Easy to handle and keep.**

✘ **Difficult to source.**

Norfolk Grey

The story of the Norfolk Grey is one of those 'almost, but not quite' sort of tales. It's a breed of chicken that, in many respects, should have done much better than it actually did. It was created by a man called Fred Myhill from Norwich sometime between 1910 and 1912. His vision was to develop a dual-purpose farmyard fowl that would be a hardy and robust producer of both eggs and meat. It's not clear whether Myhill had any great ambitions for his creation to become a widely-used commercial breed but one assumes that he was hoping for as much success as possible.

As far as the actual development process is concerned, it's not clear which breeds were used. There was certainly some Game influence, and it seems likely that the Leghorn played a significant role as well. However, Myhill's development plans took a serious knock with the arrival of the First World War. He, like so many others, went off to fight in France, and the resultant four-year absence caused real problems on the home front. The birds had apparently been breeding true at the time he was forced to leave but, while he was away, things started to slide. Virtually all of his careful selection work was undone as the birds were allowed to free-range as they pleased, breeding with all and sundry.

So upon his homecoming in 1918 he was greeted with the disappointing news that his poultry project lay in tatters, and he faced the prospect of having to start virtually from scratch once again.

Inauspicious start

This he did and, having re-established a workable flock of reliable breeding stock, he decided to 'go public' with the breed and entered some birds at the Dairy Show in 1920. But 'Norfolk Grey' wasn't the name under which these first birds appeared. Instead, Myhill chose to call them Black Marias. Presumably this

A Wattles should be long, bright red and finely-textured. Face and ear lobes need to be the same colour. Watch for signs of white in the lobes. This is a bad sign and is definitely something to be avoided if you plan to exhibit, as it represents a serious breed fault.

B The comb must be well-serrated and ideally show four or five spikes that are separated by equally deep 'troughs'. It's very important also that there are no side sprigs, and that the comb is upright and straight. Sometimes there can be a tendency for them to curl or kink at the back. Also, avoid those showing 'fish tails', which is where the trough between two spikes is too shallow.

C Always look for a good, dark eye that's either dark brown or black. There was a bit of a spate of light green-eyed examples occurring a few years ago, but these seem to have been successfully bred out more recently. It's a point worth checking, nonetheless.

D Male Norfolk Greys like this one must show a clear silver hackle that extends right the way around the front of the neck, forming an unbroken mantle.

E Look for a reasonably long and flat back, and clean saddle feathers. Discolouration can be a problem in this area. Exposure to bright sunshine can cause a yellowing of these feathers. A straw-colour can also appear here for genetic reasons and birds showing this don't make good breeding stock. Saddle feathers can be smutty too; another undesirable feature.

F Male Norfolk Greys should present a good, full-feathered tail with a pair of sickle feathers plus plenty of side hangers. The tail shouldn't be held terribly high on male birds, and is even lower – and a good deal smaller – on females.

G All black feathers should show an attractive beetle-green sheen under the right lighting conditions. Males can show white feathers at the base of the tail, which isn't a good feature, although it's rare.

H Being a productive utility fowl capable of laying well over 200 eggs in a season, the Norfolk Grey shouldn't be fluffy around the thighs and abdomen. Feathering generally is fairly tight around the heavy, stocky body.

I Dark slate or black legs, free from feathers, with similarly-coloured, four-toed feet are another breed essential. Occasionally, lighter-coloured legs will crop up, but these are to be avoided, both for breeding and showing purposes.

J Males should have a clean, black breast with no silver flecks. Some silver feathering here is acceptable on females. Breast should be full and rounded, indicating good table qualities. Avoid birds showing a 'cutaway' breast.

name had occurred to him during his time in France, as it was a slang term used by British soldiers for describing a large German artillery gun, and the black smoke-generating shells it fired. The name failed to strike a chord in England and, in about 1924, Myhill decided that a rethink was necessary, and switched to the altogether more appealing 'Norfolk Grey'.

Regrettably, even this failed to trigger a significant upsurge in the breed's popularity. Perhaps it was simply a matter of poor timing; having to compete against the then 'big hitters' of the purebred utility poultry world – such as the Rhode Island Red, the Sussex and the New Hampshire Red – was simply asking too much. The Norfolk Grey did develop a reasonably strong following among farmers in the county but, in reality, that's just about as far as it went. The interwar years passed and the arrival of WW2 heralded more hard times for the breed – so much so, in fact, that by the late 1940s references in the poultry press to the Norfolk Grey (and appearances at shows and exhibitions) had completely dried-up.

The suggestion is that Myhill gradually lost interest in the breed himself and that, following his death in the late 1950s, the primary driving force for its survival was lost. There followed a gap of about 20 years during which time the Norfolk Grey was all but forgotten during the 1960s and '70s. That it was not entirely lost was primarily thanks to rare breed enthusiast Roland Axman, who brought the Norfolk Grey back from the brink of extinction.

Being a Norfolk man himself, Roland was aware of the Norfolk Grey, although at that stage he'd never actually seen a live one! But while on a trip to the Malpas poultry show in Shropshire during the early 1980s, he happened to spot a trio of these elusive birds. He discovered that the owner lived in Stoke-on-Trent, contacted him and found that they'd been supplied by a Reverend Bowden, from Gloucestershire. A call to him revealed that stocks were low, but that he'd be happy to provide some hatching eggs, or even birds, the following year.

Good male comb should be straight and have four or five spikes. A good dark eye is another important requirement, as are red ear lobes

However, as it turned out, Roland got a call from the owner in Stoke a few months later, with the news that he didn't want to continue with his birds and had decided to get rid of them. Roland

Side sprigs like that on the rear of this comb are very undesirable; best avoided when breeding

jumped at the chance, and wasted little time in arranging the delivery of the trio; a good cock and hen, plus another hen that was too black. He bred a few birds that year but, because it was relatively late in the season, the offspring never attained their full size. The following year, though, he went to town with his breeding program and, by 1984, felt confident enough about their quality to exhibit them at the Royal Norfolk Show, and caused quite a stir.

What is it?

The birds had become so rare that many visitors to that show, and subsequent ones that Roland went to, didn't even recognise the breed. He then joined the Rare Poultry Society, and managed to organise an exhibition class for the Norfolk Grey at the National Poultry Show. Interest slowly grew and Roland was happy to distribute hatching eggs and birds to new and enthusiastic keepers whenever possible.

The sort of two-way lean on this bird's comb isn't ideal. But his wattles are a good length, and even too.

Spare males make great table birds. They will produce a 5-6lb bird on the table with no special treatment, and the meat provides lovely taste and texture

Although the book of poultry standards does detail the required weights for a bantam version, Roland has never seen one, and has no evidence to suggest that any have existed in recent times.

Nevertheless, despite the resurrection of interest the situation for potential buyers is currently very difficult. Sources of surplus birds are still extremely limited and Roland says he needds to make a concerted effort to breed more birds so, hopefully, the situation will improve somewhat.

Those keepers lucky enough to own Norfolk Greys will testify to the breed's generally active yet docile character. It's an upright type of bird, with a reasonably long body that's broad at the shoulders. The body is generally well-feathered with moderately tight plumage, has a full and rounded breast and the wings are carried well tucked. The tail on male birds should ideally feature a pair of curved sickle feathers plus a good number of side hangers.

The head sits atop an abundantly hackled neck, and features a short, curved beak, a large and bold eye, a single, upright comb, a smooth face and long, fine wattles. The comb should be well-serrated with four or five spikes and a firm base. The whole bird stands on shortish but strong legs that are set further back than on many other breeds. The shanks are featherless and the feet have four toes.

As far as plumage colour is concerned, if you're not a fan of black and silverwhite, then perhaps the Norfolk Grey isn't the bird for you because it's only available in the one, essentially black and white colourway. The male bird is the more striking of the two sexes, with silverwhite feathering on the neck (hackles have black striping), back, saddle, shoulders and wing bars. The rest of the plumage is solid black and the legs are dark too; either a slate-black or, preferably, completely black. So the only splashes of real colour come from the headgear and face, which are bright red, and the attractive beetle-green sheen on the sunlit black feathers. The eyes and beaks are dark and horn-coloured respectively.

The female is essentially black all over, apart from the neck hackles that have some silver-white fringing, and the throat area, which is delicately laced with the same colour. The comb and wattles are correspondingly smaller on hens, so the areas of red are less apparent than on the male.

Hardy and friendly

Generally speaking, the Norfolk Grey presents a friendly and calm character. As with most breeds, though, you do come across the odd cockerel that can be a bit sharp at times, but these aren't terribly common. In the main these birds are easy and pleasant to handle, and well-suited to the back garden environment.

The 'farmyard fowl' heritage

AT A GLANCE

Size
Heavy

Origin
Norfolk, UK

Weights
Male – 3.20-3.60kg (7-8lbs)
Female – 2.25-2.70kg (5-6lbs)

Egg laying
230+ pa

Colours
Black and silver-white

Legs must be as dark as possible. Avoid any that you find with light-coloured scales. Feathering on the shanks is a real no-no

ensures that the Norfolk Grey remains a hardy bird that's perfectly capable of dealing with inclement weather without too much trouble. If conditions under foot become damp and muddy for a time, then these birds will bustle through and carry on pretty much as normal.

While they *can* fly, they aren't known as 'fliers', so high fencing to keep Norfolk Greys enclosed isn't going to be necessary. In most cases you should find that a four or five-foot netting fence will be perfectly adequate as a barrier for keeping birds in place.

One consequence of the Norfolk Grey's rarity is that the few breeding programs there are have, out of necessity, been forced to rely on high levels of inbreeding. Consequently there simply isn't the fresh blood to inject any meaningful amount of vigour, and this certainly has a detrimental effect on fertility and hatchability levels. As a result, it's usual to expect nothing much better than a 45% hatch rate. Roland reports that, although the inter-breeding necessary hasn't caused him any specific problems, it is vital to be very careful with stock selection; there's no point in breeding with anything other than the very best birds you have, otherwise quality will rapidly and catastrophically fall away. It's also important with these birds to hatch reasonably early so that the chicks are up and running before the end of May at the very latest. Birds hatched after this time tend not to achieve the desired size before the cold weather arrives, and never catch up thereafter.

Youngsters are impossible to sex at an early age, and it's not until around about the three-month mark that differences start to become apparent. The most obvious pointer is usually that male birds will grow the odd silver feather on the back, while the females will stay completely dark.

The Norfolk Grey isn't known as a sitter, and it's only very occasionally that a hen will turn broody. But the docile character means that mixing with other breeds isn't usually a problem, and

The female Norfolk Grey is a much plainer looking bird than the male. It's essentially black although there is some silverwhite detailing on the neck hackle feathers. Undercolour on both sexes should be grey. A good hen will produce 230 eggs in a season

cases of bullying within the flock are very rare indeed.

There's good news on the vice front too, as the Norfolk Grey presents no cause for concern, not having a reputation as a feather-pecker or an egg-eater. Disease doesn't tend to be an issue either;

the breed's hardiness means that it isn't particularly susceptible to any of the common poultry complaints, so ownership at a day-to-day level is just about as straightforward as it can be.

So readers attracted by the practical prospects of this useful rarity can look forward to keeping a no-nonsense and genuinely useful utility fowl. While outward appearances may not be sufficient for many to set the pulse racing, the practical value of the Norfolk Grey should be. Then, perhaps even more importantly, there's the conservation aspect. This is a breed that continues to struggle for its very survival. Without more serious keepers prepared to take on and breed the Norfolk Grey to the accepted standard, it's long-term future could be bleak.

YES OR NO?

✔ Very hardy.
✔ Pleasant character.
✔ Impressive layer.
✔ Good table bird.

✘ In very short supply.
✘ No bantam version.
✘ Plain appearance.
✘ Low hatch rates.

The Norfolk Grey will make a well-mannered, docile and productive addition to any back garden; it's finding them in the first place that's the problem!

Orpington

For a friendly, docile and interesting chicken, there are few breeds that can beat the Orpington

"There is no breed of modern production in which so much interest is taken, or over which there has been so much controversy, as the Orpington." These views were expressed by Mr W Richardson from Horsham, Sussex, in 1911, and offer an insight into the importance of this desirable British breed.

Created by William Cook and named after the Kentish town where he lived, the black Orpington was the first to arrive in 1886. Cook had set out with the simple objective of creating what he considered to be the perfect all-rounder. He wanted a heavy, soft-feathered bird that would offer great utility performance (good eggs and meat), possess a practical level of hardiness and look attractive too. His 'building blocks' were the black Minorca male and the black Langshan female; the black offspring from this cross were then mated with black Plymouth Rocks.

Black Orpingtons are the second most popular large fowl, and the favourite bantam. It's important that they show a good, beetle-green sheen to the feathers, but avoid those with a purplish tint

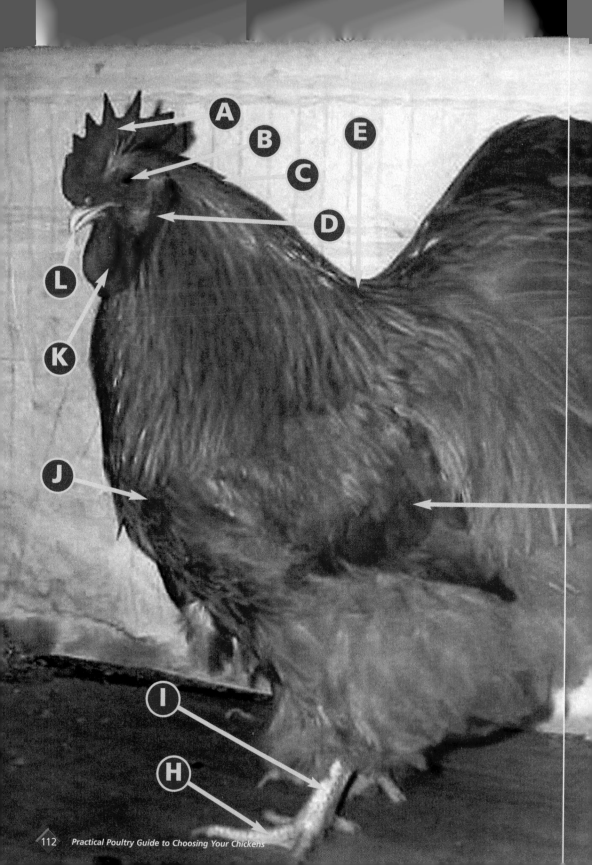

F

G

A Watch for side sprigs on the Orpington's single comb, which should have five even serrations and must follow the line of the head at the back – flyaway combs are undesirable.

B The eye should be bright and active, with a good strong red colour in the buff and white; dark brown on black and blue examples. Avoid a 'dull eye' on buffs and whites, where the eye appears a washed-out, light brown colour. The eye should be bold and round in all cases. Avoid 'droopy eyes' on the buffs – a condition where the skin around the eye hangs too loose below the eye (this has appeared on strains bred in Germany).

C On buffs, watch for a black undercolour on the back of the head, immediately behind the comb. You'll need to search for this by lifting the feathers. It's a bad point, and is usually linked with black smuttiness in the bird's tail.

D Any white in the ear lobes is a serious fault as far as exhibition birds are concerned.

E An Orpington's back should be short. This is a genuine physical feature rather than an illusion created by the profuse feathering. Good examples will show a curvaceous U-shape, formed between the neck, back and tail, as in this case.

F Look out for black smuttiness in buff tails – very easy to spot. Coarse feathers here, or anywhere else on the bird, are another bad point to be avoided.

G The Orpington is a non-flyer with small wings that should be held tight to the body – avoid droopiness or 'dropped' wings.

H Feet must have four, well-spaced and straight toes. Yellow colouring on the feet is to be avoided.

I Inspect legs for signs of feathering (especially on buffs and whites), which is a serious fault. The scales should be clean, but feathering does occur and is probably an indicator that the strain has been crossed with Cochin at some point. Legs mustn't be too long and should not show any yellow.

J Avoid birds that are 'split-breasted'. This is a condition that's easily recognised as the plumage shows what appears to be a parting down the line of the breastbone, with the feathers sweeping away to either side. This seems to occur most on the blacks. Also make sure the breastbone is straight on large fowl Orpingtons. Deformities can be caused by birds being allowed to use perches too early in their development. This is obvious to feel when handling the bird. This problem can also relate to a genetic defect, so birds with it are best avoided.

K The wattles should be an even length – unevenness is something to be avoided. All head gear on a healthy bird should be bright red.

L The beak should be a good horn colour (on the buff), not crossed and showing good contact between the upper and lower mandibles along their entire length ('open beaks' should be avoided).

Utility roots

But Cook's original creation was a very different bird to the feathery monster we know today, as the 1890s photograph included here illustrates. Further colour varieties followed; white (1890), buff (1894), Jubilee (1897, celebrating Queen Victoria's Diamond Jubilee), spangled (1900), cuckoo (1907) and blue (1908) and a red, although the last three were not created by Cook himself. However, of these seven varieties, only four survive today as standardised colours – black, white, buff and blue.

The Orpington was an almost instant success, and certainly ranks as one of the most popular breeds of all during these early days. The black was exported all around the world, and the buff followed suit. The white, however, was a slower starter, failing to catch the public imagination in the same way as the other two, darker varieties.

The near universal popularity of the new breed ensured that thriving clubs were established for enthusiastic keepers and, of course, rivalries between these organisations inevitably arose. The first was the Black Orpington Club, and this was followed by the rival Variety Orpington Club, that aimed to cater for the other colours. This latter organisation took the white under its wing but, because the club never really flourished, the white's general appeal remained limited as well. It took the formation of a specialist White Orpington Club to really give this colour the kick-start it needed some eight years after its introduction.

Another club arrived in 1952, catering for the newly-created bantam Orpington versions and then, in 1972, this was merged with the Black Orpington Club, with the new organisation being called the Orpington Club (back to the original name established in 1887). This, together with the Buff Orpington Club that was formed in 1898 (now the largest single-colour breed club there is), remains in existence today and both clubs continue to operate happily, successfully and without rivalry.

However, the way in which the breed has been transformed into a profusely-feathered 'showman's special' would, I'm sure, leave William Cook far from pleased. The breed's utility performance has been lost almost completely. Early breeders wasted little time in mixing-in Asiatic breeds, such as the Cochin, in an effort to increase feather profusion. But this, of course, came at the expense of laying performance.

While there are still a few utility strains of buff Orpington in existence, the majority of birds around these days will prove to be poor layers. Long gone are the days when a healthy Orpington hen would produce 200 eggs in a season. Even today's best utility example will only lay 120 or so and, if you get any more than 50 out of a feathery exhibition strain, you'll be doing well.

So the Orpington isn't now a breed to opt for if you're after a healthy egg supply for a hungry family. It's a breed to be kept for its impressive looks and wonderful character. Of the standardised colours the buff is the most popular colour among enthusiasts today, followed by the black, then the attractive blue. The white has been through a decidedly sticky patch but, recently, has enjoyed somewhat of a resurgence thanks to imported stock from Germany. The cuckoo, Jubilee and spangled are now extremely rare.

New on the scene are a crop of laced varieties which, although attractive and certainly popular with many domestic keepers, are somewhat frowned upon in breed club circles. While keepers will undoubtedly continue experimenting with, and selling, these differently-marked versions, it seems unlikely that any will ever be accepted or officially standardised by the clubs.

Today's examples

The modern Orpington large fowl is a big bird, with the male blacks and blues weighing not less that 10lbs (4.55kgs) apiece. It presents a bold, upright and graceful form, with a deep, broad and 'cobby' body shape. The back is fairly short, while the breast is deep and rounded. The wings are small, and carried tight to the body, and the tail is short and compact, flowing and held high. The bird sits on strong, widely-spaced short legs, with the thighs almost hidden by feathering.

The standardised black, buff and white colours are pretty straightforward, but the blue is rather more intricate. It has an attractive mix of soft, slate-blue and black, and there's pretty lacing on the female. In many respects this colour has the look of an Andalusian about it.

Legs, beak and feet are white on

This shows a comb that's not particularly good – it has uneven serrations plus a fly-away rear section. This bird is also showing an eye colour that's a little on the light side, and some bagginess in the skin around it

This male shows a more desirable comb. In addition, the eye is darker and better too

the buffs and whites, and dark blue or black on the blue and black. Eye colour varies too, being red/orange on the buffs and whites, and very dark brown or black on the two darker versions.

Regrettably, the large fowl Orpington isn't a particularly easy breed to buy at the moment, if you're after top-quality, exhibition stock. The number of experienced breeders producing good birds is

limited to little more than a handful for both the two most popular colours – buff and black. The blue is even more difficult to track down simply because it's such a hard colour to breed well. Keepers working to the standard have to be ruthless with their birds to ensure top quality, and there are only a few prepared to live with this level of 'wastage' as they seek perfection. Consequently, very few of the blues you're likely to come across will be particularly good. The white is perhaps even rarer at the moment, although an influx of German stock has prompted something of a renaissance.

Of course, if you're not terribly worried about buying Orpingtons that accurately reflect all aspects of the breed standard, then you'll find things a lot easier in terms of sourcing stock. There are plenty of enthusiastic breeders around producing and selling stock of varying quality. But, as with everything else, you pays your money, and you takes your choice!

The most popular Orpington bantam is the black, and the great demand for this colour means that there are plenty of dubious examples being offered for sale. Be particularly aware of overall size; there is a definite tendency for the blacks to be bred far too large. You should be looking for a bird that is about one quarter the size of the large fowl and, if you're in

Orpington weights
Large fowl male:
Blue – not less than 4.55kg (10lb)
Black – not less than 4.55kg (10lb)
Buff – not less than 3.60kg (8lb)
White – not less than 3.60kg (8lb)
Large fowl female:
Blue – not less than 3.40kg (7.5kg)
Black – not less than 3.60kg (8kg)
Buff – not less than 2.70kg (6kg)
White – not less than 2.70kg (6kg)
Bantam male: 1.7kg (3.75lb)
Bantam female: 1.5kg (3.25lb)

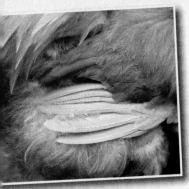

Wings should be small and tightly held to the body. Avoid birds where the wing appears to have dropped, like this

any doubt, then check the bird's weight against the information included in the table on the opposite page.

Buff bantams have deteriorated somewhat in quality over the past five years – to such an extent, in fact, that good examples are now very hard to find. Whites and blues are not as popular, which is presumably why they remain the hardest bantam colours to source.

Practical poultry?

The Orpington is a generally hardy breed, and will enjoy a free-range lifestyle given the chance. However, it's very important to note that an outdoor lifestyle will detrimentally affect feather colour on buff and white examples. The sun's rays have

The blue is a very attractive but hard-to-breed Orpington colour option. It is standardised but there are few breeders happy to deal with the 'wastage' required to produce really good ones like this

a bleaching effect on these feather colours, causing buff plumage to become randomly streaky, and

white feathers to adopt 'strawy' or 'sappy' appearance – they turn a dirty yellow colour. While this isn't a desperate problem from a breeding point of view (it's not a genetic condition), it obviously represents a serious defect in the eyes of an exhibition judge.

However, take care not to confuse this sun-induced discolouration with patches of white that may be found in wing feathers of buff Orpingtons. This is a more serious genetic problem, and birds showing it really are best avoided.

To avoid feather discolouration, top breeders and exhibitors either keep their birds indoors, or let them run in the fresh air in an

A wry tail, where the tail feathers point noticeably to one side or the other like this, is another characteristic best avoided. 'Squirrel' and 'dropped' tails are other faults to watch for

Large fowl Orpingtons, whatever the colour, are prone to toe curling (sometimes referred to as 'buckle toe'). This tends to be a condition caused by the sheer size and weight of the bird – the outer and rear toes flatten, and turn outwards

Here is some typical white patching in a buff's wing feathers – not a good thing from a breeding point of view

environment that's completely shaded from direct sunlight. The damage to buff plumage can occur surprisingly quickly, with two weeks exposure being all that's needed to promote it. The situation with the whites isn't quite so severe, with feathers taking two to three months to turn yellowish.

The famously placid and docile nature of the Orpington has led it to be described as 'the ladies' breed'. For this reason it's a bird which has found much favour among the aristocracy and indeed, royalty. Both males and females remain easy to handle and manage at all times of the year, and you'll even find males perfectly

approachable during the breeding season. The Orpington really is a superb garden bird for the family environment,

Bullying isn't really an issue either, and males and females can be mixed perfectly well without serious problems. There may be some initial squabbling while the pecking order is established, but everything normally settles down after a couple of days. Also, the bird is a non-flyer, making it very easy to contain.

The good news continues with the fact that Orpingtons do not suffer with serious breed-related disease problems. Just about the only characteristic trouble you'll have to watch for is parasitic infestation. The breed's profuse feathering means that external parasites, especially mites, will pose a constant threat. Consequently, keepers must remain extremely

vigilant, adopting careful inspection routines and regular anti-mite treatments as part of their husbandry and welfare programs. Pay particular attention to the key areas under the wings, around the vent and on the back of the head and neck.

Owners interested in natural brooding will be happy too, as the Orpington hen makes a great broody and an excellent, attentive mother. Despite their size, the hens aren't clumsy birds, so broken eggs are a rarity.

So, if you're searching for a friendly, engaging and interestingly historic pure breed, then you really should consider putting the Orpington very near the top of your wish list. Just about the only drawback is its poor laying performance but, that aside, it's a breed that can be thoroughly recommended.

The white Orpington all but disappeared here in the UK but, thanks to new stock from Germany, it's now enjoying a resurgence in popularity

YES OR NO?
✔ Very family friendly.
✔ Simple to keep.
✔ Impressive looks.
✔ Not flighty.

✘ Egg-laying performance not good.
✘ Profuse feathering harbours mites.

Plymouth Rock

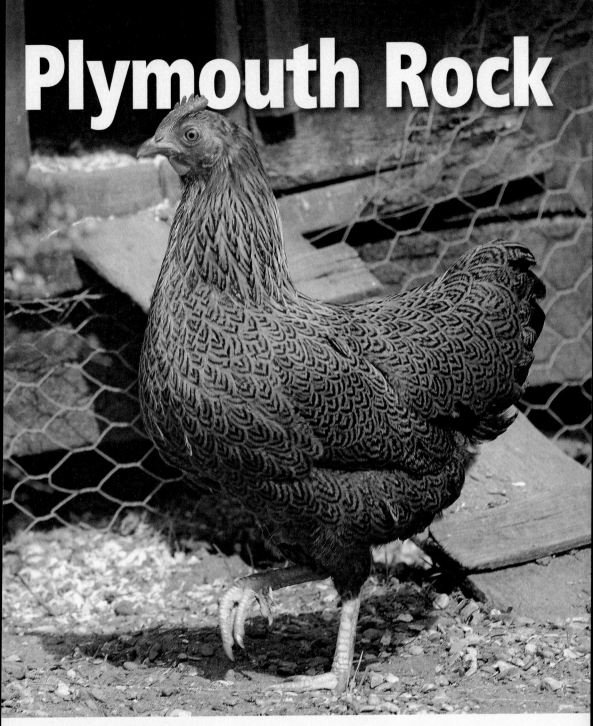

Some of the secrets to buying good examples of this extremely practical American utility breed

A bantam partridge hen

The Plymouth Rock is a popular, dual-purpose heavy breed that was developed in Massachusetts, USA, during the 1820s. But exactly how the first birds were produced remains a bit of a mystery, and so theories vary. The breeds thought to have been involved in the mix include Andalusian, Leghorn, Dominique, Cochin and Java, although nobody's completely sure.

The attractive barred version of the breed was included in the first *American Book of Poultry Standards*, published in 1874. The White and Black varieties arrived next (as 'sports'), followed by the Buff version that was apparently developed in Rhode Island.

Balanced size

The large fowl Plymouth Rock is a big but well-balanced bird, with a deep body, straightish back and medium-sized tail; everything's in proportion and attractive curves are a notable feature of the breed, particularly on the male.

There's a good range of colours to choose from, and the breed is available both as large fowl and bantam. Potential owners can pick from barred, buff, silver pencilled, columbian, partridge, black and white in large fowl. There's a similar choice available for the bantams, with the addition of blue and splash (a blue diluted colour). However, while all these colours are theoretically available, tracking down good examples can be tricky, particularly if you're after large fowl. These are very thin on the ground in anything other than the most popular barred, buff and white plumage colours.

The large fowl Plymouth Rock really enjoyed its UK popularity heyday during the immediate post-war period, when commercially-bred buffs competed impressively in laying trials against 'big hitters' such as the Rhode Island Red and Wyandotte. However, once the ration-led shortages really started to bite, the popularity of keeping large Rocks as backyard fowl began to wane – these birds have very large appetites! So it was at this point that the bantam version crept ahead in the ownership stakes, and it remains the most popular option to this day. The buff and barred varieties are the most widely kept, followed by the white, black, blue, columbian, partridge and silver pencilled.

The Plymouth Rock had been in existence for a good while in the USA before interest in it on this side of the pond led to the formation of the first club. Even then, the organisation wasn't a single-breed affair, being called The Leghorn, Plymouth Rock & Andalusian Club. It was founded in 1886, and another nine years rolled by before, in 1895, the breed got its own, dedicated

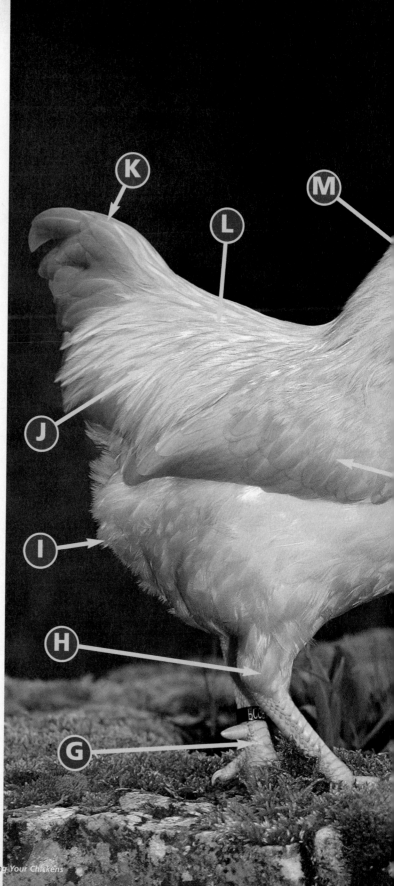

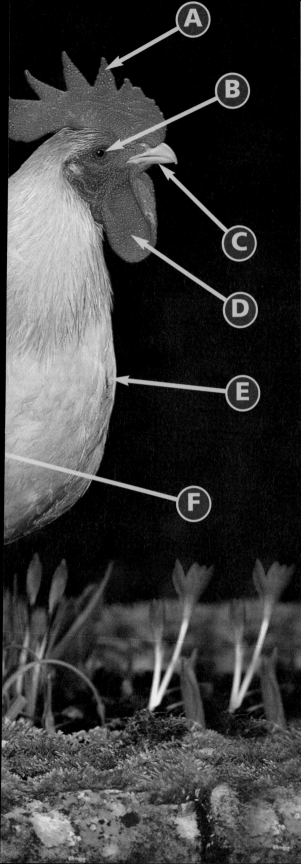

A The comb should be bright red, single, straight and five-pointed. Avoid 'fish tails' where a single serration peak splits into two. Watch for side sprigs at the back – a bad point. The rear of the comb should curve down, following the line of the back of the head. Comb should be very small on the female.

B In all plumage colours, the eye should be large, bright and prominent, showing a rich bay colour (red).

C The beak should be yellow in all colour varieties, although it can present some horn colouring on partridge birds. It's medium-curved and stout.

D The wattles on the male bird should be rounded and of medium length; not too elongated. They are much smaller, and more rounded on the female.

E The breast of a good Plymouth Rock should be deep and well rounded. Avoid those which present any sort of cutaway.

F Wings are medium-sized and should be carried high and tight in against the sides of the body. The tips of the flight feathers should ideally be covered by the saddle hackle feathers.

G Legs should be stout and strong, with four straight toes on each foot. All should be straight. Colour should be yellow to match the beak, but there should also be red spotting down the outside of each leg. The deeper yellow the leg colour, the better. Yellowness can fade on hens that are laying hard. The males should retain good colour at all times, however this does vary from strain to strain. Diet can be an influencing factor too. Avoid 'willow legs', which are tinged with pale green.

H It's important for a good Plymouth Rock to show some thigh like this. Too much feathering will obscure this, which is wrong. This applies to both large and bantam versions.

I Feathering generally should be tight, with no excessive fluffiness evident, even in the vent area. If buying barreds, look for good, straight barring and avoid solid black feathers, especially in the wings. The buff colour should be good and even across all areas.

J Saddle hackle feathers should be of a good length and abundant.

K The tail should be compact on both male and female birds, with good rise. Avoid feathering which curls over on female birds (a little bit like an Orpington). The tail should not rise higher than the bird's head, so that overall appearance remains in proportion and balanced. Avoid black peppering in large buff females, and white in bantam.

L The Plymouth Rock is all about sweeping curves and this should be particularly apparent on the male birds, with the neck, back and tail forming an attractive sequence. The female has a flatter back than the male. Unfortunately, emphasis placed on bantam plumage marking on the barred versions means that type has suffered; many now are very narrow.

M Medium-length neck with attractive curve and good neck hackle. Ideally this feathering should extend right round the neck, although a narrow gap at the front under the beak is permissible.

Plymouth Rock Club (barred Rocks only). Buff Rocks arrived from America in 1897 – imported by James Bateman – and were accepted by the club in 1900. The White followed soon afterwards but then things on the club front started to become somewhat disjointed. A series of breakaways saw a number of separate clubs created for the individual colours, plus additional organisations in Scotland and Wales. Then, in 1912, a further option, The Plymouth Rock Society, was born.

Bantams became part of the main club around 1920, but this then prompted even more factions to divide-off, establishing separate, bantam-related clubs. Ultimately, though, all this unrest came to nothing as, in time, every single breakaway group returned to the fold, and re-amalgamated with the parent club.

Hardy character

The Plymouth Rock was bred for its hardiness, a requirement that was vital in the often harsh North American climate. So, from a practical point of view, it's a fairly rugged character that isn't going to be fazed by inclement weather, frost or snow. This makes it a relatively straightforward breed to keep; it's a no-nonsense type of bird with few foibles to trip-up the less experienced keeper.

Laying performance, while not as strong as it once was, remains pretty impressive by pure breed standards. The buff bantam can be a particularly good performer, with healthy young hens capable of producing 230+ eggs in a season. What's more, they are quite capable of continuing to lay well into the winter months without the need for supplementary house lighting. The large fowl aren't quite so prolific – a good pullet will probably lay 180 in a season – but, of course, the eggs are much larger. Winter performance can be increased with additional lighting but, left to their own devices, large fowl will cease laying during the darker months.

The Plymouth Rock's docility must rank among its most appealing characteristics, from the

Good, evenly-serrated male bantam comb

A bad, 'fly-away' comb which fails to follow the head line

domestic keeper's point of view. These birds don't have a flighty bone in their bodies, and so can be easily contained by fences no more than four feet high. This placid nature also makes them a favourite for the family environment; they are great with children and will become very tame if handled frequently and well.

So, in a nutshell, all the Plymouth Rock requires of its keeper is a good level of poultry husbandry. Given enough space, dry and clean housing plus a regular, balanced diet, these birds will be your friends for life.

For those potential keepers with one eye on the future, the Plymouth Rock is a relatively easy bird to breed. Fertility levels in

bantams are normally pretty high, so you can expect good hatch rates. The position with large fowl isn't quite so encouraging, though. The relative rarity of these birds means that a fair bit of inbreeding takes place, particularly among barred flocks kept by exhibitors. The inevitable, knock-on effect of this is a fall-off in fertility, meaning that successfully breeding large fowl can be more of a struggle. For some reason, the situation isn't quite so bad with either the large buffs or the whites.

Great broodies!

Both bantam and large fowl hens make excellent broody mothers although, in some respects, this can be a bit of a drawback for those keen on egg production. The females (especially the partridge versions) will go broody very quickly if eggs aren't collected promptly, interrupting their laying schedule. From a straightforward size point of view, bantam hens tend to work more effectively as broodies. The large fowl versions, especially the buff, can be a little on the heavy side, and prone to clumsiness.

As far as productive life is concerned, Plymouth Rocks will go on laying well into their fourth or fifth year, although numbers obviously fall away dramatically at this age. The large fowl birds should live happily into their sixth year, while bantams can live on even longer, surviving for anything up to eight or nine years. The one cloud on the horizon, as far as the big ones are concerned, is that they face the risk of running to fat. This is particularly the case for birds that don't enjoy the benefits of a free-ranging lifestyle with plenty of exercise. Their large appetite can take its toll on birds kept in confinement, so careful management is required to avoid unnecessary problems.

Overall, though, there's very little to worry about in terms of disease and serious illness. Just about the only recognised problem you're likely to encounter is Mycoplasma;

Good feather shaft colour (right to the skin) is an important aspect of buff Rocks

Good depth of undercolour on the saddle is a key requirement for buffs

the Plymouth Rock is prone to it. This is definitely something to watch out for when buying-in stock, with the tell-tale signs to look for including gurgling sounds from the lungs as the bird breathes, and swollen eyes. Neither Marek's disease or Cocciodosis are any more common with the Plymouth Rock than they are with anything else.

So, if you're looking for a bird that's interesting and productive to own, yet relatively straightforward to keep on a day-to-day basis, then the Plymouth Rock takes some beating. Why not get in touch with the breed club, track down your nearest recommended breeder and go and see what you think?

Plymouth Rock bantams make excellent broody hens and very attentive mothers

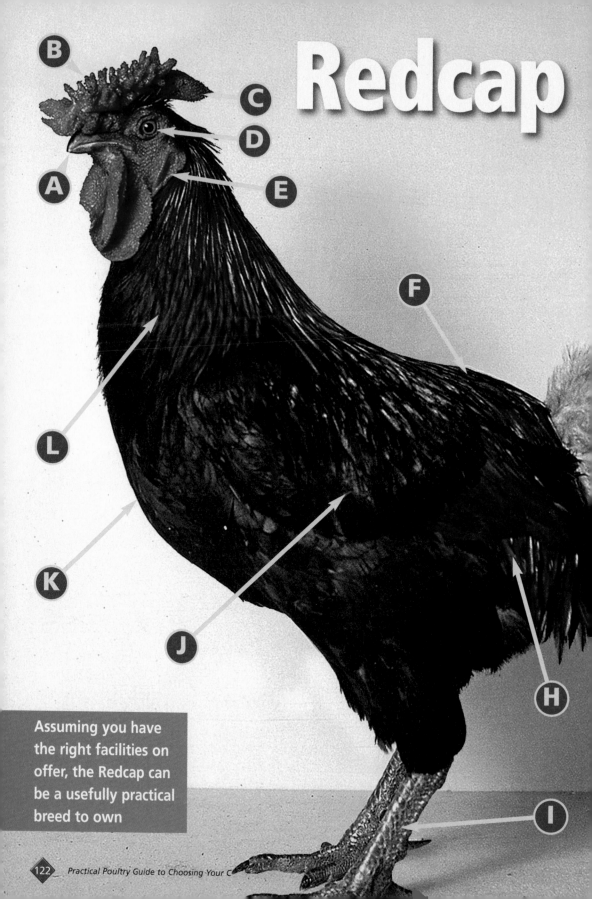

Redcap

Assuming you have the right facilities on offer, the Redcap can be a usefully practical breed to own

There aren't too many breeds which still show a largely intact original breeding purity. Most have been crossed with this and that as breeders – and, more often than not, exhibitors – sought to enhance or exaggerate what fashion dictated as the most desirable attributes at the time.

But the Redcap has somehow managed to escape most of the ravages of the collective Fancy and remains much as it was hundreds of years ago. This, in itself, is an intriguing aspect of the breed,

and just one of many reasons why it's worth serious consideration as an ownership proposition.

Uncertain origin

But there's mystery in the story too. Nobody's quite sure where the Redcap originated, or why it never caught-on in the southern counties; the breed was traditionally a favourite farmyard fowl in northern England. Some point to links with the Hamburgh, while others suggest that the Redcap is related to the Old English Pheasant Fowl traditionally kept in Yorkshire. Old names for the Redcap include the 'Manchester', 'Moss Pheasant' and 'Yorkshire Redcap', but its popularity in the Peak District led to it becoming known as the Derbyshire Redcap; an informal name that's still widely used today.

Whatever its roots, the Redcap is a fine looking bird that offers a very

A The Redcap's beak should be medium length and always predominantly horn-coloured.

B The Redcap takes it name from this impressive rose comb. It must sit squarely on the top of the head, and not hang down on either side to obscure the eyes. The top of the comb must be covered in many short spikes (workings), and shouldn't show a pronounced indentation running from front to back on the top. Mature male birds like this one have a comb that's twice the size of the female's.

C This rearward-facing spike is called the 'leader', and it's important that it points straight out towards the bird's tail, rather than being angled down to follow the line of the head/neck.

D The Redcap's eye should be red, full and prominent, and never overhung by the comb.

E Face, wattle and ear lobes must all be bright red, matching the comb. The red ear lobes are interesting as they separate the Redcap from the other two other breeds it's most closely linked to; the Old English Pheasant Fowl and the Hamburgh both show white lobes. Any white in a Redcap's ear lobe is a serious fault.

F The back of both the male and female Redcap should be broad, moderately long and angled slightly down towards the base of the tail.

G The male's tail is full and typically carried at an angle of 50°, while the female's is held slightly shallower (60°). Watch for squirrel (too vertical or leaning forward) or wry (leaning to one side or the other) tails; both are serious faults.

H On male birds, the rich, 'bronzy' colour of the saddle hackle feathers should ideally match that of the neck hackle.

I Legs and feet must be lead-grey and the feet must have four toes. Crooked toes can be an issue, although it's not terribly common. Legs must also be completely free from feather and set well apart.

J Wings are a moderate size and are held close to the body. Check also for white tipping on primaries and secondaries. Hen feathers should have a black spangle tip (which shines with a beetle green sheen in the sunshine) in the shape of a half-moon. Black lacing sometimes occurs on the feathers and this is a fault to be avoided. Birds showing this will not be pure, having been crossed with another breed sometime in the past. Also watch for 'sootiness' on the feathers.

K The breast should be full, rounded and black on both male and female birds. Take time to check the straightness of the breast bone when handling any prospective purchase.

L The neck should be of moderate length, pleasantly arched and well feathered.

practical level of dual-purpose, utility performance. While not famed as a great sitter, the hen is a good layer of reasonably-sized, white-shelled eggs, and presents very attractive, black-spangled, rich-brown plumage. As a meat producer the breed is pretty impressive too. A mature male will reach nearly 3kg in weight, and the meat is tasty and succulent, with a slightly 'gamey' flavour to it.

But it's the Redcap's ability to survive in harsh environments which really endeared it to the farmers of northern England. Utterly at home in the wild conditions of the Yorkshire Pennines and Derbyshire Peak District, this breed proved ideally matched to an energetic, no-nonsense, free-ranging lifestyle.

But probably the most distinctive feature of both male and female Redcaps – indeed, it's where the name comes from – is their impressive, bright red, rose-type comb. Although only about half the size on the female, these combs are covered with small spikes (workings) in both sexes, and can measure anything up to 8x6cm on a mature male bird. Each also features a pointed leader; a rearward-facing spike that extends straight out from the back of the comb.

There's an appreciable difference between male and female birds as far as plumage is concerned. There's a lot of black on the male, with only the neck, hackles, back and wings showing any red/brown colouring. In contrast, much of the hen's feathering features a rich, nut-brown ground colour with a very attractive black, crescent moon-shaped spangle at the very tip of each feather. Primary and secondary wing feathers should also show a two-tone colour scheme, being black on one side of the shaft and red/brown on the other.

Faces, wattles and ear lobes should be bright red, to match the comb. The eyes are red/orange and prominent, while legs and feet need to be a uniform, lead grey colour. Overall, the Redcap is a graceful, well-balanced and very attractive looking bird. There are no other colour options.

Above: Study of a mature male Redcap showing comb with good, straight leader and a bright eye

Left: This is a bad comb; it's obstructing the bird's eyes

Stock sourcing

The relative rarity of the Redcap means that sourcing good stock can be a problem. Although there are about 60 members in the enthusiastic Derbyshire Redcap Club spread across the UK, only a handful of them exhibit their birds and it's these keepers who tend to be the most prolific breeders. Not many enthusiasts seem to run large flocks, which means that most of them are reluctant to sell stock simply because they are hatching so few birds themselves. Nevertheless, the club does appreciate the need to promote the breed, and will certainly do its best to assist new enthusiasts with finding good stock.

Both large fowl and bantam versions are available although (somewhat unusually in this day and age) the popularity of the bantam is nowhere near that of the original fowl. They first appeared during the 1950s but only a few club members keep them today.

There's a popular belief that much of the Redcap's utility performance has been lost due to breeding designed to enhance the size of the comb. However, those inside the club disagree, maintaining that the bird remains a genuinely practical choice. It's said that a healthy Redcap hen is today capable of producing between 160 and 200 eggs in a season, which is certainly pretty good by pure breeds standards.

Much depends on the conditions in which the birds are kept. It's very important to appreciate that they don't tolerate confinement well, and are happiest when allowed to

The Redcap hen is brighter and more attractively-marked than the male bird, with a rich, nut-brown ground colour and pretty black spangling (not laceing) on the tip of each feather. The spanglingt should ideally be half-mood-shaped, and glow with a beetle-green sheen when viewed in bright sunshine and. They are good layers too

Legs should be a solid, lead grey. The brown tinges visible here are not right for show purposes

free-range over a sizeable area. Redcaps love nothing more than being able to forage, and hens that are kept in a small run are unlikely to prosper, and egg numbers will fall progressively, well below the totals already mentioned. Perhaps it's this aspect of the breed's behaviour which has led some people to make false judgements about a deterioration in overall laying performance.

The Redcap is certainly a hardy breed that will deal happily with virtually all weather conditions.

Primary and secondary wing feathers should be two-tone; one side of the shaft being black and the other side brown. Watch out for those white tips – they're to be avoided if you are entertaining ideas of showing

This black 'sootiness' is also a fault to be avoided

A very useful consequence of this rugged, toughness is that the breed doesn't suffer any specific disease problems at all. Redcaps aren't prone to any of the common poultry conditions and, assuming good levels of husbandry and welfare, will serve their keepers with commendable and productive reliability.

Quiet a character

The Redcap's character is perhaps most aptly described as wilfully flighty. For this reason, it's important to realise that this breed isn't ideally suited to the first-time keeper, or those living in an urban environment. While the birds are certainly friendly enough and, with plenty of handling, will be happy and comfortable in a family environment, they do need plenty of space to thrive. So if you're looking for a placid, relatively inactive breed for a smallish town garden, then the Redcap is *not* the bird for you. Keeping these birds in place requires fences that are eight feet high; they are good fliers and seem to be able to climb too!

Generally, though, assuming you have the necessary environment to offer, Redcaps are relatively easy and trouble-free birds to keep. They breed readily too, producing strong chicks, although the hens are not famed for their broodiness. Having said this, when the odd one does turn maternal, you'll be able to rely on her as a good sitter.

It's perfectly possible to run Redcaps in a mixed flock, although anyone contemplating this should be aware that the large fowl males are big, strong birds that won't hesitate to exert their authority over rivals. Fighting can be an issue requiring careful management.

The rarity of the breed today means that there's an increasing, money-making trend to label birds in auctions as 'Redcaps' when they are nothing of the sort. Recently, birds with single combs and a complete lack of feather spangling have been spotted at sales masquerading at pure Redcaps. So it really is a case of 'buyer beware'.

However, find yourself a handful of good quality birds, allow them the luxury of a large free-range, area and you certainly won't be disappointed. The Redcap's sparky

Bantam hens can go too dark overall...

...or too light, with not enough spangling. Both extremes are best avoided if you're serious about breeding to the accepted standard

character endows these birds with considerable appeal, and it's a breed which tends to instil tremendous loyalty once you've been hooked!

YES OR NO?

✔ Very hardy.
✔ Not prone to diseases.
✔ Impressive layer.
✔ Good table bird.

✗ In short supply.
✗ Don't like confinement.
✗ Good fliers.

Rhode Island Red

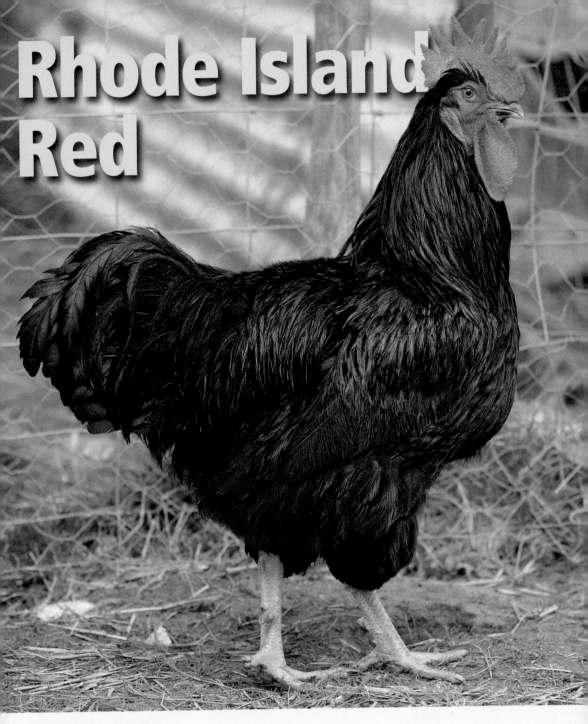

The Rhode Island Red is a famous and influential American chicken breed that was created by mixing indigenous fowl with imported birds from the Far East. Like the Wyandotte and the Plymouth Rock, the 'Rhodie's' mixed-bag of ancestors led to it becoming known as a 'composite breed' – something it shares with others from the UK

and Europe, including the Orpington, the Faverolles and the Marans.

But it's the Rhode Island Red that is probably the most famous and successful of the lot, having developed an impressive reputation for both its egg-laying and meat-producing capabilities. It also played a fundamental role as a building block in the development of the modern hybrid and, as such, established for itself a place in poultry history as one of the truly great breeds.

Look for the distinctive, half-and-half, black/red colouring on the wing feathers

East meets West

Work on developing the breed began towards the end of the 19th Century, when breeders in the Rhode Island area of New England, on the North American east coast, set themselves the task of producing a dual-purpose bird of genuine excellence. To do this they crossed local strains with a selection of more exotic, imported breeds, including the Shanghai, Malay, Java and Leghorn.

Legs should be yellow or horn-coloured, with four, straight toes on each foot. Watch for signs of feathering on the legs

A A head that's carried slightly forward is an RIR characteristic. The face, wattles and ear lobes should all be bright red. Any actual white on the lobe is a serious failure point.

B A good Rhode Island Red should show a prominent, clear, red eye. Paleness is something to be avoided. Poor examples can sometimes show a yellowy-green coloured eye, which is a bad sign. A white eye should definitely be avoided.

C The RIR originally featured a rose comb – reflecting its Asiatic roots – but the single-comb version soon took over as the most popular. Watch out for side sprigs, or a comb that falls significantly to one side or the other. Rose-combed examples are available, but are very rare in the UK.

D Ideally the beak should be medium sized, slightly curved and yellow. Horn colouring like this, with some darker patches, is perfectly acceptable.

E 'Type' (shape) is a key factor as far as the RIR is concerned, with one of the most important requirements being a flat, almost vertical breast line. Obvious roundness here should be avoided.

F Female RIRs tend not to be as glossy as the males, particularly as they get older. Where black does show, however, it's important that is possesses that characteristic beetle green sheen. Be on the lookout for pure white feathers; not a good sign. Also, watch out for feathers that are too fine, or even 'frizzled'; a sign that too much breeding emphasis has been placed on achieving lustrous, dark feathering.

G Any sign of feathering (actual or evidence of plucking) on the shanks, especially on bantams, is bad. Feet should have four well-spaced and straight toes. Crooked toes can be a problem, but the so-called link between their occurrence and the use of infrared heat lamps at the rearing stage is anecdotal.

H Wings should be of a good size, but carried close to the body and so that the flight feathers run horizontally. In recent years the breed has suffered with an outbreak of 'split wing', so watch out for primary feathers hanging noticeably lower and more angled than they should be.

I The tail should play an important part in the overall look of a Rhode Island Red. Ideally it's held almost flat, thus accentuating the length of the back, and enhancing the rectangular look of the bird's body.

J Check for the presence of a roach (humped) back, which is a genetic deformity, and thus to be avoided. It can be particularly prominent on the RIR because the back is normally so straight and flat.

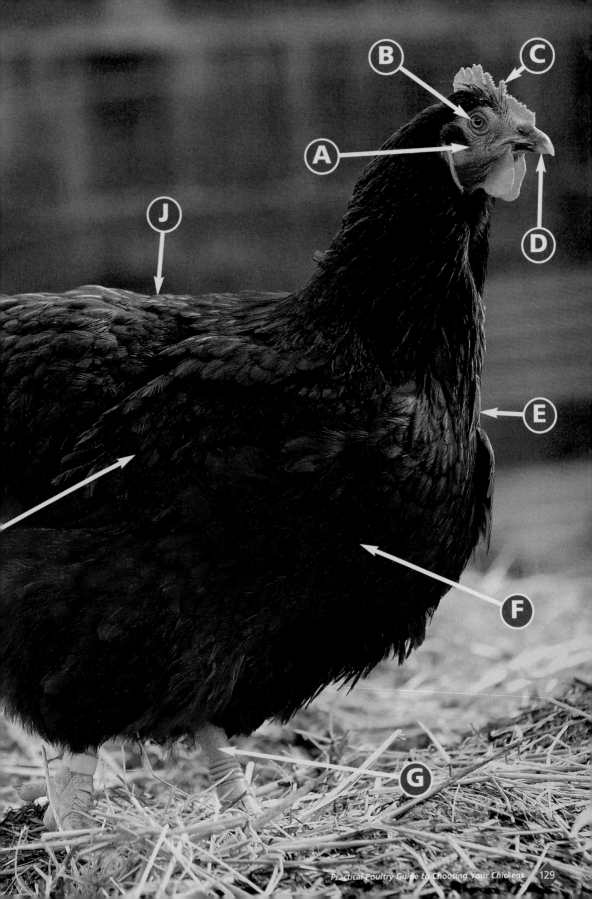

AT A GLANCE

Size
Large, heavy, soft feather

Origin
America

Weights
Male - 3.85kg (8.5lbs)
Female – 2.95kg (6.5lbs)
Bantam male - 790g-910g (28-32oz)
Bantam female - 680-790g
(24-28oz)

Egg laying
170+ pa

Colours
Rich red/black

Bantams are more popular than the large fowl nowadays; they require less space and are cheaper to keep

With their specific objectives firmly in mind, the breeders took care to make their breeding selections on utility grounds alone, crossing the best males and females to maximise egg production and size. Following successive years of carefully controlled work that never veered from its results-based criterion, patterns among the best-performing birds became evident and a characteristic 'look' emerged – the Rhode Island Red had arrived

The earliest birds had rose combs, and were exhibited at a poultry show in Massachusetts during 1880. But a single-combed version followed (presumably as a result of introducing the Leghorn into the breeding mix) and then, by 1906, both types had been standardised in the USA.

A club for RIR keepers in Britain was established in 1909, and is still going strong today, though the breed's heyday seems long past in the UK. At its peak of popularity – probably during the 1950s and '60s – countless breeders across the land kept the birds very productively, for both utility and exhibition purposes. Nowadays, however, although the UK breed club remains a strong and active organisation with 100 or so members, the number of serious breeders within the ranks has fallen. The single comb dominates these days, although there are only perhaps a couple of experienced breeders currently working with them in the UK. The bantam version, which was created here early last century, is probably now more popular than the large fowl. Much of the development work for

this was overseen during the 1920s by Lord Greenaway at Stanbridge Earls Poultry Farm, near Romsey in Hampshire.

As a consequence of this gradual loss of interest, there's a belief in RIR circles that the examples we have today are inferior to those of 40 years ago; they're lacking in key areas such as overall type, colour and wing marking. Of course, as

overall numbers fall away, the cycle of decline inevitably gains momentum. The fewer birds and experienced keepers there are, the harder it becomes to breed consistently to the required standard.

Pretty birdie

On a more positive note, one of the secrets of the Rhodie's great

Good undercolour extending right down to the skin is an important point. Ideally its colour should match the top feathers, but this is a rarity these days

Any grey showing in the undercolour is a problem, and is best avoided in birds intended for the breeding pen

appeal, apart from its very useful dual-purpose potential, is its pretty, 'traditional' appearance; it looks like a proper chicken should! The breed has become famous for its rectangular profile (if you discount the legs and neck!); something which many, somewhat unflatteringly, liken to a brick. When viewed from the side, a good RIR hen is certainly more oblong than square, thanks to a long, flat back, only slightly raised tail and vertical, flat breast. However, the breed isn't as red as it used to be, or as its name might suggest. Today's examples offer an attractive combination of rich, reddy-brown and black.

Hens should show a rich, lustrous colouring, although the desirable sheen will certainly fade with age. The black feathering they have (some in neck hackle and tail) will be less apparent than on the male birds, but should still show a beetle-green luminescence in the right light. Males tend to have a more glossy and darker overall appearance and, in both sexes, the undercolour should be as close as possible to the top colour. These days, though, good matches are extremely rare, with most birds being significantly lighter below the surface feathers. Grey smutting in the undercolour (especially around the shoulders) is something to be avoided, although a degree of black smutting can work in your favour, from a breeding point of view – it will help produce a rich top colour in the offspring.

Wing feathers should be distinctly marked with black on the outer half of the primaries, and on the inner half of the secondaries. In both cases, the opposite side should be clear red, with no sign of dark peppering. 'Spotting' on these wing feathers is virtually impossible to get rid of, so birds showing it shouldn't be used in a serious breeding program.

The RIR's eye should be full, prominent and bright red, contrasting well with a yellow or horn-coloured beak. Ideally, the legs need to be yellow too, but a

The male head tends to be dominated by the single comb, with its 5-6 serrations. Those at the front and rear tend to be smaller than those in the middle

reddish-horn colour is perfectly acceptable as well. Yellowness in the leg is more likely on birds that free-range on grass, but is something that will fade with age.

The breed's decline in the popularity stakes over the past 40

Black 'peppering' on the wings like this is a bad sign and is something to be avoided on show birds

years means that buying good examples now is probably harder than it's ever been. According to the club, it seems that we're down to just a handful of experienced breeders producing top-quality stock, in either large fowl or bantam form. Consequently, it's more important than ever for those seeking good birds to do so through 'official channels', via the club. However, it's also worth noting that the few notable breeders who do remain aren't producing birds by the hundred, so supplies are always going to be limited. Pure breed poultry is never an 'off the shelf' commodity at the best of times but, in the case of the Rhodie, new customers should certainly expect a bit of a wait when ordering stock.

Good value

Prices are likely to vary a bit too, depending on where you buy. But the fact that the RIR doesn't tend to be such a popular show bird now means that really high, demand-driven prices are rare. Typically, you can expect to pay £50-75 for a good breeding-stock trio, be they large fowl or bantams (2009 prices). However, significantly higher prices have been recorded at pure breed sales and auctions, although it must be remembered that the quality can vary enormously from these sources.

One other point worth making is that there's a commercial laying strain of Rhode Island Red available, which is very different from the pure-bred, exhibition type. These birds are lighter in both build and colour, with much of the look of a typical, light-brown laying hybrid about them. Don't be confused by this, and buy one expecting the other!

But the potential buying struggle is worth it because the pure-bred Rhode Island Red remains a great bird to own. It's very hardy and loves a freeranging lifestyle. The flipside of this, though, is that the large fowl aren't very well suited to confinement, and have a tendency to go downhill if kept this way. Bantams are far more tolerant in this respect.

The breed benefits from a very quiet, docile character. Flying isn't a problem to worry about with the large fowl, so enclosure fencing needn't be any more than four feet high, assuming you don't have a fox problem. Bantams can be a little more flighty, and the cockerels will often have a spiteful streak too. This is definitely something to watch for in the domestic environment, particularly if young children are involved. Another consequence of this is that poorly kept bantams, with insufficient space, can be prone to feather pecking,

The docile nature of the large fowl means that they are always easy to handle and a pleasure to live with. They have no special requirements with regards to feeding or welfare. Fertility levels are always good, assuming you're working with a decent strain, of course. The chicks are strong and feather-up well, although they

aren't particularly quick growers. A cockerel will typically take nine months to mature for the show pen; pullets are somewhat quicker, at six months.

The large fowl hens can make good broodies, but their weight and tendency towards clumsiness can cause problems. While keepers find them ideal for reliably hatching duck and goose eggs, the thinner shells of their own eggs means that breakages are a little too common. Consequently, most breeders use incubators. Bantams are markedly less broody than their large fowl counterparts, so these don't really offer a natural brooding option at all.

Disease resistance is generally good too, but it has been suggested that the RIR's large size can be a factor in an increased rate of fatal heart attacks. While this seems to be a bit of a breed characteristic, over-feeding and lack of exercise – both problems that can affect birds kept in a confined, domestic environment – certainly won't help matters. An excessive build-up of fat around the heart and other primary organs can lead

to premature death. It's not unusual for aging RIR hens to reach 10lbs (4.5kg) in weight, which is very large. If this is combined with high levels of internal fat, then there's often only one result.

Don't let this dampen your enthusiasm, though. The Rhode Island Red remains a fantastic option for the domestic keeper. It offers traditional looks, useful egg-laying performance, a rugged yet docile character and great potential as a table bird too. What's more, it's a breed in need of assistance, and thoroughly deserving of continued preservation.

YES OR NO?

✔ Dual purpose.
✔ Traditional looks.
✔ Good layer.
✔ Hardy.
✔ Disease resistant.
✔ Ideal beginner's bird.

✘ Supplies limited.
✘ Bantam males can be spiteful.
✘ Hard to breed for exhibition.

The Rhode Island Red is an ideal starter breed because of its calm character. The large fowl are easy to handle and a pleasure to live with

Rosecomb

One of the poultry exhibition scene's lesser-known little gems!

The Rosecomb isn't a hardy breed, and most experienced keepers only allow their birds out on rare occasions. Male birds take about nine months to mature fully, at which point keepers then have a window of showing opportunity that lasts little more than eight weeks if they're lucky! Females mature slightly more quickly, in six to seven months

The Rosecomb is a member of an exclusive group known as the 'true bantams'. All of these breeds (which include Belgian, Japanese, Pekin and Sebright among others) are characterised by the fact that they have no large-fowl counterpart. It's designated as a British breed, but whether or not this is actually the case is hard to say. There are a number of varying accounts about the breed's origins, which make it difficult to be certain.

Some suggest it was brought to Europe from the Far East (Java) and developed here, while others claim that it's little more than a miniature Hamburgh, that was created in Holland. Then there are those who believe it to be a genuine British breed, that's existed and been carefully bred in the UK for hundreds of years. Specialist researchers believe they've discovered documentary evidence to support this last idea, and point towards literary references, which appear to indicate that the Rosecomb's existed here ever since the late 1400s.

Pretty survivor

One thing's for certain, though, and that's that this diminutive little breed is one of the longest-established that we have. However, it's also important to realise that the wonderful, jaunty bird that we see today is probably a far cry from whatever its ancestors would have looked like. The 'modern' Rosecomb is a product of the exhibition Fancy; that dedicated group of enthusiastic breeders and showmen who, over many decades, strove to fashion birds into forms they thought desirable. You can argue until the cows come home about the rights and wrongs of 'creating' a breed in this essentially artificial way, but few can take issue with the fact that the result is

a stunningly individual-looking bird. The males, in particular, present a superbly neat and curvaceous appearance that's instantly attractive. What's more, in many respects, it's probably just as well that the original breeders were so successful in their aims, as it's almost certainly the Rosecomb's show appeal that has guaranteed its survival as a standalone breed to this day. It offers no utility performance to speak of and so, in essence, has nothing but its looks to offer.

As we'll see later in this feature, this bird is a difficult one to show at the highest level – getting them to the show pen unscathed is a tall order, even for the most experienced breeders! Add to this the fact that a good Rosecomb will 'blossom' like a prize bloom in its first year, and then fade to a shadow of its former glory thereafter, and you can start to appreciate that this is no ordinary breed of chicken. The

A Wattles should be neat, rounded, finetextured, even on both sides and free from creases.

B The beak colour should match the legs. As dark as possible on black birds; white on the whites. Watch for and avoid crossbeaks.

C Rose comb must be broad and flatfronted, tapering to a fine point at the end of its rearward-facing leader (the whole thing is triangular when viewed from directly above). Workings on top of the comb should be a mass of fine, rounded spikes that, overall, form a flat surface, rather like coral. Comb must also be free from significant ridges, troughs and side sprigs, and extend forwards to about half way along the beak. It shouldn't drop down at the sides to cover the eyes.

D Ideally, the leader should be round in section, not 'bladed', and should rise at an angle of about 45°, although lower angles are still acceptable. Those angled downwards, following the line of the neck, are best avoided.

E Eye needs be as dark as possible. Black is ideal to aim for, but dark red or hazel is acceptable. Avoid birds with light orange eyes. Face must be red with no white showing, especially near the lobe.

F The ear lobe is a key feature of the Rosecomb. It should be pure white and as round, thick, finely-textured and flat as possible – looking as though it's been stuck on to the side of the bird's head. Avoid birds with lobes that are noticeably dome-shaped or dished.

G Back should be short so that a pleasing U-shape is created between the neck and the tail. Ideally there should be plenty of feathering on the saddle.

H Black feathers to show a good beetlegreen sheen. Avoid those with purple barring as this is a sign of poor breeding. The tail furnishing feathers should be broad, plentiful and show rounded ends.

I Main sickle feathers must be a good length and width on birds that are to stand any chance in the show pen. They should trace a bold sweep, enclosing the main tail feathers.

J The legs are short and should be as dark as possible on the black birds (light on the white). The shanks are short too, and free from feathers. Each foot should have four toes – missing nails are to be avoided.

K Wings need to be held tight to the body and at an angle of about 45°, so that the tips point towards the ground and cover much of the shank. Avoid birds that hold their wings too high, exposing all the thigh.

L A prominent and well-rounded breast is another key aspect of a good Rosecomb. Avoid those which are cut away.

Good feather width like this is a sign of a well-bred Rosecomb, albeit rare these days

A good Rosecomb male head

Rosecomb isn't a 'starter bird', and probably isn't best suited to the novice keeper who fancies keeping a few birds in the back garden. But for those who wish to take the exercise more seriously, keeping and exhibiting Rosecombs will often become an all-consuming passion.

Cobby customer

For one so small and 'cobby' (round and compact in build), the Rosecomb certainly manages to pack a great deal of visual interest into its being. The bird is dominated by its especially striking head, featuring an impressive rose comb and dazzlingly white ear lobes – both key aspects from a judging point of view. The neck sweeps down to a very short back, which forms the base of a pretty U-shape, the other side of which is outlined by the tail. Male birds are especially impressive in this department, with luxuriantly curved sickle feathers that sweep over in a graceful arc.

Another dominant curve is that of the breast, which is both full and rounded when the bird stands well. The upright and almost pugnacious effect is heightened by the angle of the wings, which should be held at about 45°, with their tips pointing towards the ground and covering portions of the thigh and shank.

The Rosecomb is available in three standardised colours – black, white and blue – but a number of additional plumage options have become available in recent times,

including birchen, Columbian and black-red. However, it's the black that remains the most popular colour and it's certainly the showman's favourite. This is perhaps because the bird looks at its most striking in this colour, especially around the head. The bright red comb, wattles and face contrast beautifully with the jet black of the feathering, plus the white of its lobes.

But, as I mentioned before, this state of visual perfection with a good Rosecomb is transitory. The first moult is a significant moment in a male showbird's life because once the big tail sickles are lost, they never grow back to the same extent. The eye-catching ear lobes can be problematic too, as they seem particularly prone to blistering and other damage on this breed. Keeping them in perfect, unblemished condition for any length of time is all but impossible, especially if the birds are allowed outside; even the sunlight will turn them off-white! All these factors combine to make the Rosecomb one of the most challenging breeds to rear for the show pen, which is why the aficionados get so hooked on them.

Yet, somewhat surprisingly, despite the relative speciality of the Rosecomb, the prices you can expect to pay for examples of the breed aren't that high. There's a good number of breeders spread across the UK who'll be happy to

Watch out for a condition known as 'feather grizzle', which causes an unsightly, ragged feather edge. It appears to be caused by the feather sheath failing to fall away on time

It's probably true to say that few other than the most ardent enthusiast would describe the Rosecomb as genuinely friendly. Typically, these birds display a feisty character; both males and females can fight among themselves if newcomers are mixed into an established group. Space is important if you want to minimise this. The combative nature means that owners need to take care during the breeding season, when the males can become aggressive. I've heard tales from breeders who've been attacked when entering their birds' pen at this time of year. But the positive aspect of this is that the most pugnacious males tend to be the most fertile. So if you've got one that comes at you with flashing claws and beak, at least you know he'll be 'filling' the eggs!

Those of you considering taking on the Rosecomb should also note that it's a good flier so, if you plan to allow the birds into a run, then it'll need to be secure. At a practical level, and inclement weather tolerance aside, these birds don't suffer with any characteristic ailments, so should lead essentially disease-free lives assuming welfare and husbandry levels are up to scratch. However, Rosecomb hens don't make particularly good mothers, and aren't known as reliable sitters (relatively tight feathering is an issue here, too), so most breeders work with an incubator. Keepers interested in natural brooding are best advised to rely on the services of a recognised broody hen, such as a Silkie or an Orpington.

sell for around £20 (2009 prices) each the sort of birds that would do well at a local, agricultural-type show. However, if your showing ambitions are higher, and you fancy securing a Best of Breed award at a club event, then you'll be looking at £35+ for top-quality stock.

Delicate disposition

While the Rosecomb is a relatively straightforward breed to keep, it could never be described as a hardy one. Like other true bantams, it's a delicate little bird and although happy to range outside during fine weather, wet and cold winter conditions prove much more of a challenge. These birds are more susceptible than most to the effects of wind chill,

and so many owners opt to keep their stock inside most of the time. An outdoor lifestyle really is off the agenda if you're serious about showing, primarily because it greatly increases the chances of cosmetic damage to the all-important headgear (comb, lobes and wattles). However, older birds – with their showing exploits behind them – can become more hardened to life in the open air.

Even those birds kept inside need to be somewhat molly-coddled. While no breed likes in-house draughts, the Rosecomb seems particularly sensitive. With this in mind, some breeders even resort to the careful use of heaters during the coldest winter months to keep their birds comfortable and happy.

You don't keep Rosecombs for the size of their eggs. However, you can expect about 200 each season from a healthy young hen of the small, white-shelled eggs like these two being compared to a large fowl egg

Scots Grey

A

B

C

D

K

J

I

G

H

The much-neglected
but surprisingly
practical Scots Grey
is a breed with much
to offer

There are very few breeds of domestic chicken which still remain more or less exactly as they were 200 years ago, but the Scots Grey is one of them.

Its agricultural Scottish roots, combined with the fact that it never caught the imagination of the poultry Fancy at large, saved it from the clutches of the exhibition fraternity – those show enthusiasts who did so much to change the characteristics of so many of the popular breeds during the late 1800s.

While the breed was exhibited locally in Scotland, including shows in Edinburgh, its popularity faded dramatically towards the end of that century. Consequently, the bird we have today retains much of its original form and function; the Scots Grey truly is an unspoilt, no-nonsense breed. It's historic too, which should appeal to many potential keepers.

Females have much smaller single combs. A good hen will lay 120 eggs a season

Tangled roots

As with so many other types, the precise origins of the Scots Grey remain a bit of a mystery. Known locally in Scotland as the 'Chick Marley' this breed was also once referred to as the 'Scotch Dorking', a name which has given rise to theories that it is in some way linked to the English Dorking. But, although it exhibits a good deep breast and appreciable width of back, the fact that five-toed examples never seem to occur makes

A Head should be bright and alert, with red comb, ear lobes and wattles. Comb is single on both males and females (small), with good, even serrations. Watch out for white in lobes – a bad point.

B Eye should be bold and bright; red/amber in colour.

C Beak is white on the male, horn/white on the female.

D Back should be broad and flat. Large fowl Scots Grey, like this, should be big – males 7-8lbs, females 5+lbs. Feathering should be tight, not profuse. Saddle, tail and hackle feathers on the male should show a more V-shaped barring.

E Tail should be broad and full, with plentiful sickle feathers in the male. The two main sickles should show even, 'V' markings all the way down to the skin. Female tail fairly upright, with good, clear barring and feathers tightly held. Watch for, and avoid, birds with 'wry' tails (where the tail is angled to the right or left, when viewed from directly above) or 'squirrel' tails (feathers leaning forwards over the back, and pointing towards, or even touching, the head).

F The Barred Rock has been used by breeders in the past in an effort to improve the Scots Grey's barring, and this can result in yellowish legs and feather fluff (on thighs and around vent) – all bad points.

G Wings are relatively short, and should be held well tucked into the body. Ideally, wing feathers should be evenly and clearly barred, and there should be no white feathers at all. The odd black feather is better to find than a white one.

H Legs are long, enhancing the bird's erect, active appearance. Hocks visible, and legs free from feathers. Male birds should have pure white legs with tight scales. Spurs will need to be controlled as they grow constantly, and get very sharp. Females should have light legs too, although they can be dusky as pullets, and should also develop black spotting as they get older. This mottling darkens with age. There are four toes on each foot, but watch for 'duck-footed' examples, where the rear toe is raised off the ground. This is undesirable, and causes balance problems.

I The body as a whole must feel solid when handled. Although classed as a soft-feather breed, a pure Scots Grey should be tightly feathered with no profusion evident at all.

J Breast should be deep, full and well rounded.

K The neck is reasonably long, arched in the male with profusion of clear, V-shaped barred hackle feathers – avoid white in these feathers. Female neck feathers tend to be darker and, if they can show a beetle-green sheen on the distinct black barring, so much the better.

Scots Greys are least happy inside, so make sure they have plenty of room, avoiding overcrowding. It's an active breed that loves to roam

this idea somewhat unlikely. The breed's long-legged, upright and active characteristics, plus its tight feathering and solid feel, also suggest breeding connections with the Old English Game but, once again, no actual records appear to exist.

Despite its somewhat 'agricultural' background, there was sufficient interest in the Scots Grey to justify the formation of a dedicated breed club in Scotland, in 1885. Bantam versions of the large fowl have been around for hundreds of years too, and have traditionally been more popular than the originals outside their homeland – purely because their size makes them easier for many enthusiasts to keep.

There's only ever been one colour of Scots Grey, although its description has changed a little over the years. Originally it was described as being 'cuckoo-coloured', but is now classified as having a barred plumage pattern.

It's very important that the feather barring extends right down to the skin, and that the undercolour remains an even blue/grey, not white

The ground colour of the whole body, plus the thighs and wings, should be a consistent steel grey/blue, and each feather is barred with clearly defined black, horizontal bands that should all display a metallic lustre. On male birds, this barring is more V-shaped on the long neck hackle feathers, saddle and tail. The barring on the

females tends to be a little wider, which gives the hens a darker look overall.

The clean, lean lines and sharp markings of both the male and female birds are attractively offset by the bright red comb, ear lobes

Avoid any examples you find with a 'wry tail' like this. This is a bad breeding fault

White feathers in a wing like this are bad news. Check prospective purchases carefully

and wattles. Both sexes feature a single comb, although it's larger on the males, upright and with good, even serrations. This, coupled with the white legs (mottled with black on the female) and light beak, gives this generally underrated breed a striking and distinctive appearance.

Rarity value

The Scots Grey remains on the Rare Breed Survival Trust's watchlist, classified as 'endangered'. So, although the situation regarding the overall number of birds is now healthier than it was 30 years ago, it continues as a breed in need of enthusiastic support. In reality, of course, this shouldn't be a problem as the Scots Grey has plenty to offer the domestic keeper. So quite why it remains on the fringes is a mystery.

Good Scots Greys will provide their owners with just about everything they could wish for from a domestic fowl. Admittedly, they won't break any records with their egg laying – a good hen produces about 120, medium-sized eggs a season – but that's just about their only 'weakness'. The breed has never really been selected for its egg laying ability but, instead, was bred as a rugged, durable crofting-type fowl intended to weather the Scottish climate as well as produce reasonable quantities of eggs and meat.

On the plus side, the breed offers tremendous hardiness thanks to the countless generations of forebears that scratched a sparse existence on Scottish hillsides. Scots Greys are active, alert and very 'streetwise'. They certainly won't simply stand and stare as a fox approaches, but will be quick to take evasive action before trouble strikes.

The birds are adaptable and will tolerate most conditions, apart from a tightness of space. The large fowl need room, and aren't best suited to small-house living, when their active nature can lead to problems. Under these conditions, the bantam version would be the sensible option. What's more, contrary to widely held opinion, the hens (in both large and bantam forms) do go broody and make good mothers. It's also not unheard of for the male birds to lend a hand with rearing duties too.

The bantam and large fowl types share the same characteristics as far as behaviour is concerned. They are friendly, talkative birds (the males tend to be noisy!) and individuals can become great characters. The breed mixes well with most other domestic poultry, and adult birds tend not to suffer from bullying. However, it's worth noting that the males are slow developers, and so remain on the small side for longer than some other breeds. This means they can get picked on in the early stages. They tend to look rather weak and feeble all the way up to about 20 weeks old and then, in the following month, they show a dramatic growth spurt and really blossom. For this reason, it makes sense to rear Scots Greys on their own, to avoid any risk of trouble.

White beak, bright red headgear and barred plumage give the Scots Grey male a striking, crisp appearance

The fact that the Scots Grey is relatively rare means that sourcing good examples is more difficult than it is for more popular breeds. In addition, the males are generally at a premium. Breeders often tend to be quite particular about who they let birds go to; with good stock being reasonably scarce, people are keen that their birds should go to very good homes.

An almost perfectly-marked Scots Grey male wing

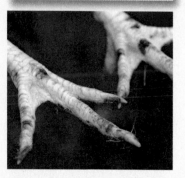

This is the sort of black mottling you should find on the legs and feet of pure-bred adult hens. A yellow colour indicates breeding impurity

Tough nut!

Another advantage of the Scots Grey's 'crofting' roots is that it's a tough bird that resists all the common chicken diseases well. It's not known as a breed that suffers with Marek's disease, and just about the only thing that can bring it down are respiratory problems brought on by overcrowding in poor quality housing. But this, of course, will affect just about any breed if husbandry and welfare levels are low.

In general, though, the Scots Grey is a very undemanding breed to keep, giving it the potential to be a pretty good 'starter fowl' for new keepers. The only exception to its typically friendly nature comes during the mating season, when the males become feisty. At this time of year owners – particularly those with young children – should be wary when trying to handle their birds. The males also grow long and very sharp spurs if allowed to do so, and keeping these in check is also a very good idea.

Finally, for those of you inclined to do so, the Scots Grey makes a wonderful roasting bird. Although not the biggest in out-and-out weight terms, the meat the males provide is fine-grained, very juicy and extremely tasty. •

Scots Grey females (foreground) have generally wider barring, which gives then a darker overall appearance

Sebright

Gold Sebright male – watch for too much black on the head

What to look for in one of these striking and characterful birds

There are few breeds of chicken that can match the eye-catching, crisp splendour of a good Sebright bantam. These little works of poultry art have immense appeal and, consequently, a loyal following among fanciers and domestic keepers alike. The combination of its active, jaunty character and wonderful laced plumage makes it a hard breed to resist if you're in the market for a bantam. Couple this with the Sebright's 'true bantam' status (it has no large fowl counterpart) and its 200-year history, and you have an extremely attractive proposition in all respects.

The Sebright was developed and named by Sir John Sebright in the early 1800s. He was an influential character (and an MP) who set out with the straightforward aim of producing a laced bantam. It took him many years to get it right. Sebright also established a club for his creation in 1815; an organisation which is thought to have been the first of its kind.

A The male bird's combs must feature a single, rearward-pointing leader which, ideally, should point slightly upwards.

B The eye should be prominent and dark.

C Beak needs to be a good horn colour, short and slightly curved.

D Wattles and ear lobes should be bright red. Slight whiteness in the lobes on young birds is acceptable – it often grows out as the bird ages.

E The breast should be broad and prominent, enhancing the strutting appearance.

F The wings are relatively large in comparison to the bird's overall size, and are carried low and angled down towards the legs and ground.

G Legs must be as short as possible, slender, free from feathers, well spaced and slate grey in colour.

H The four toes should be the same slate grey as the leg – watch for deformities.

I Lacing should be complete on all feathers. A heavily laced male like this one is important from a breeding point of view; its offspring are likely to be 'smut-free'. Having said this, the number of perfect birds produced is always going to be extremely small. All feathers should have almond-shaped tips, as opposed to rounded, pointed or squared-off. A green sheen on the black lacing is another important requirement.

J The tail should be as 'fanned' as possible. Males shouldn't show any of the large, curved sickle feathers typically found on males of other chicken breeds. The Sebright male is what's called 'hen feathered', so neck hackling should be minimal too. Watch also for dark 'smut' in the tail feathers.

K The back should be as short and flat as possible, to enhance the bird's strutting appearance.

L The neck should taper gracefully towards the head, be held back and show a pleasing, arched curve.

Note the dark 'smutting' in the white sections of these feathers. Not a desirable quality from an exhibition point of view

Lost in time

No specific records exist detailing which birds were crossed with which to produce this startling bantam. However, popular belief has it that Hamburgh, Nankin and possibly Poland stock were all

involved, and that Sir John used a Rosecomb bantam of the period as his starting point. Sebright created just two colours – the Gold first, followed by the Silver – both with solid ground colours and spectacular black lacing around the edge of every feather.

An interesting point of note is that male Sebrights are what's called 'hen-feathered' – they don't develop the large, curved sickle feathers in their tails (or the flowing neck hackles) which are so typical of most other male chickens. This feature, while contributing to the breed's very distinctive appearance, is thought by some to have a detrimental affect on fertility. Consequently, some breeders recommend that those males which do happen to show any sign of sickle feather growth (occasionally you'll find short ones developing) are used in the breeding pen.

One interesting change that's occurred over the years is that the colour of the Sebright's headgear (comb, wattles and ear lobes) has gradually altered from a deep purple colour – termed 'gypsy-faced' – to a more conventional, redder shade (described in the breed Standard as 'mulberry').

Despite their diminutive size, Sebrights possess a strutting sense

White feathers should ideally be solid, not opaque with show-through from underneath, as we can see here

of importance. They are compact with a short back and prominent breast. The wings are large for the overall size of the bird, and are carried low, angled towards the ground.

The tail is another strong feature; it should be well spread and carried at a high angle. The absence of neck and saddle hackle feathering helps greatly with the overall effect, ensuring a very neat, trim and smooth appearance.

The bird's head is small, as you would expect, with a short beak that's dark horn-coloured on the Gold birds, and dark blue or horn on the Silvers. The males have a rose comb which should be covered with fine points, and free from obvious undulations. It narrows towards the back, with a rearward-facing leader that, ideally, angles upwards very slightly.

The Gold type is characterised by an even gold-bay ground colour combined with sharp black lacing which has a definite green sheen to it when catching the light. The Silver version is similarly marked, this time on a solid, silvery-white ground colour. In both cases, the legs and feet should be slate grey.

Non standard

Although Gold and Silver are the only two officially recognised Sebright colours here in the UK, other options have been created elsewhere in Europe. The Germans, for example, have produced Chamois, Citron, Blue and White versions. A few of these are kept by enthusiasts in the UK, but they are very rare.

Buying through the breed club is one of the secrets of getting hold of good stock. Another is not to be tempted to buy birds that are too young. The Sebright moults at least three times before the adult plumage appears, and the early sets of feathers give no clue about what the bird's final markings will actually be like. So buying a young one on appearance alone tends to be a complete gamble. Even the most experienced breeders aren't able to second-guess the way things are going to turn out.

But even sourcing birds in the first place can be a problem too, not least because there are so few breeders around the country. The

Not what you're after! Single combed-Sebrights like this do crop up now and then but that's not in the breed standard and they shouldn't be used for breeding

HISTORY IN A NUTSHELL

- **Created by Sir John Sebright during the early 1800s.**
- **Thought to have been bred using the Hamburgh.**
- **Poland ('Polish') possibly played a part too.**
- **The Gold version was made first.**
- **Sebright Club founded in 1815; probably the oldest of all.**
- **Early meetings were held in Brick Lane, London.**
- **Membership cost two guineas per bird.**

Deformed toes is another serious fault to watch for when buying

problem is compounded by the fact that most breeders only actually breed a few birds each season, so the overall number available at any one time is always going to be low. Both colours are equally popular, and most enthusiasts will keep examples of each.

From a breeding point of view, Steve Fuller (Secretary of The Sebright Club at the time of writing) advises using an incubator. Fertility levels are generally low with this breed, and it's quite common for just one or two eggs to hatch out of a dozen which have been set.

It's very rare for a Sebright hen to go broody, so they can't be relied upon for natural brooding purposes. Anyone considering this approach to hatching will need an established broody, such as a Silkie, for the all-important sitting stage. The Sebright hen's diminutive size is a problem as, even if she does manage to hatch any chicks, her tight feathering and small body mean that she's unable to sit well to keep any youngsters warm.

The laying season begins in February, and continues through to August. A healthy hen will lay one egg every other day during this period, so owners can expect just over 80 eggs or so per season. The eggs are small, of course

Delicate souls

One important factor to appreciate if you're considering breeding Sebrights is that the young chicks are delicate little creatures. They remain vulnerable to chills and colds until they are about six months old (more so than other breeds) and so levels of husbandry have to be spot-on to avoid trouble. They require plenty of care and attention, and will need dry, clean and draught-free living accommodation during this important period.

However, once they are over six months old, fully-feathered and able to be let outside, they become as hardy as any other breed. The Sebright is certainly a characterful bird. It has a personality that matches its strutting, slightly pugnacious body language, but can be very friendly too. The secret of creating tame Sebrights is plenty of handling right from the start. Birds that are treated with care and affection as chicks will grow into tame, charming adults that will be more than happy to content themselves around the garden.

The TLC aspect is important to help counter the breed's natural flightiness. Sebrights that don't receive plenty of human contact from an early age will certainly be less friendly than those which do. They'll also be more difficult to manage, and increasingly inclined to fly, meaning that containment becomes an issue. These birds do like to roost high up, so perching inside the hen house can be set at a greater distance from the ground than that with other breeds. Also, given the chance, they will happily roost in the branches of nearby trees, which is another reason why 'taming' them is important.

There are very few health issues to worry about with the adult birds. Their general hardiness makes them as resistant as anything else to all the usual problems. Marek's disease

Females adopt the same upright stance as the males

has been known to affect Sebrights, and some breeders do vaccinate specifically against it. This is something to ask about when buying, and is obviously desirable if you plan to breed.

You shouldn't encounter many problems if you intend to mix

Sebrights with an existing flock. They are generally fairly tolerant of other birds, being neither aggressive or prone to bullying. Steve Fuller, whose birds are featured in the pictures here, has a number roaming in his yard together with an assorted flock of other poultry and waterfowl, and never has a problem.

Finally, a real plus point for the domestic keeper is that the Sebright isn't a destructive bird in terms of the damage it does in the garden – so your herbaceous borders should be safe!

YES OR NO?

✔ Fantastic plumage.
✔ Family-friendly.
✔ Engaging character.
✔ Non-destructive.
✔ Will mix with others.
✔ Adults are hardy.
✔ Great show bird.

✘ Chicks vulnerable.
✘ Infertility problems.
✘ Not a great layer.
✘ Males are noisy.
✘ It's a flyer!

Silkie

One of the most striking and unique-looking poultry breeds of them all is both family-friendly and a great show bird

O ne of the greatest appeals of keeping poultry is the sheer diversity of breeds available to us – we really are spoilt for choice! Some breeds possess a completely unique appearance which sets them apart from all others, and therein lies much of their appeal. The Silkie is just such a breed.

Its most obvious feature is the fluffy, hair-like feathering which, combined with the prominent head crest, gives the Silkie an unusual and striking look. With short, feathered legs, good examples of these birds appear as eye-catching balls of fluff – and their heads are topped with a powder puff-like feathered crest just for good measure!

Then, if all that's not enough, other unusual features of this ancient Asian breed include the fact that the Silkie is one of the exclusive group of breeds with five-toed feet. The breed also boasts black skin, plus dark purple or black comb and wattles. What's more, its ear lobes can be turquoise

This black hen shows well how ragged tails can be. Great plumage!

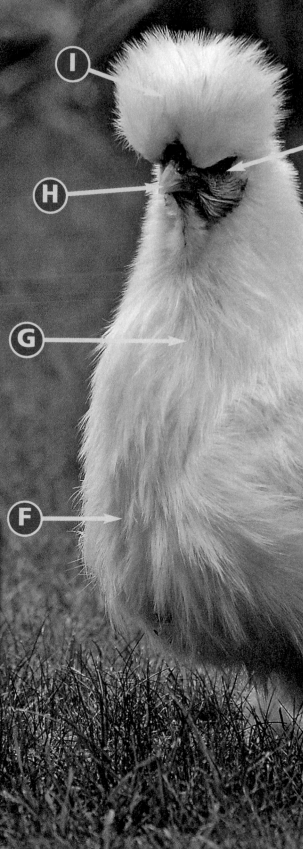

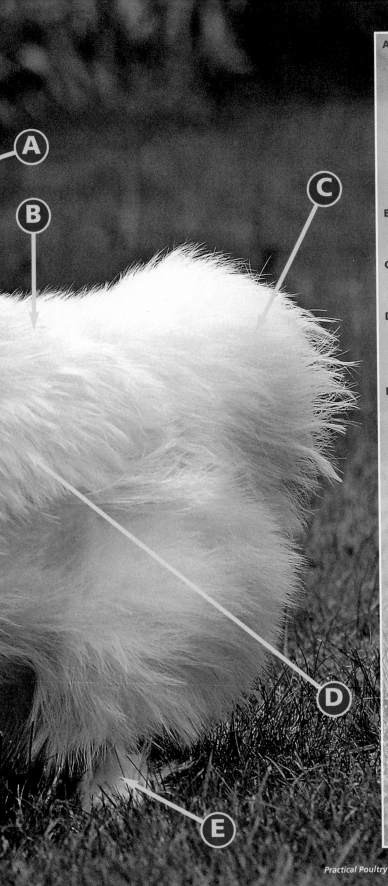

A A characteristic of the Silkie is that the face should be smooth and black/mulberry-coloured, as should be the comb, wattles and skin. A red face is a serious fault. Male birds have a much larger comb (never single) and wattles. With males, even wattle length is an important factor. Crests shouldn't be too big and the eye – which must be black – should be clearly visible.

B Silkie males and females have short backs, giving a stout overall appearance, despite the profuse, fluffy feathering.

C A hen's tail should be engulfed in a profusion of soft, cushion feathers, creating an overall shape a bit like a Cochin.

D The Silkie female presents a more rounded, fluffier appearance than the male, and is a bit neater for it. There shouldn't be a stiff feather in sight.

E Legs should be short and softly-feathered (including the feet). Avoid birds with stiff feathers on the legs, or no feathers at all. Females like this one sit closer to the ground than males, so that the underfluff is almost touching the ground. The feathered legs makes scaly leg mite harder to spot on this breed, so check birds for purchase very carefully. Avoid birds with rough or encrusted scales. Also check that each foot has five toes.

F The breast on a good Silkie should be broad, full, deep and well covered in the softest of feathers.

G The neck should be short to medium length, broad and full at the base. It should be covered with an abundance of flowing hackle feathers.

H Beak colour varies according to plumage. It should be slate/blue on white birds and dark slate on the blacks.

I The crest is the Silkie's crowning glory. On females like this it should be a fine, powder-puff affair, whereas on the male it consists of longer, rear-slanted feathers that produce a swept-back, spikier look.

blue! The dark skin means that these birds take on an odd appearance when cooked; an impression that's heightened when it's discovered that the bones inside are virtually black too!

Uncertain origin

Like so many of the other old poultry breeds, nobody is quite sure about the origin of the Silkie, but it's widely accepted that the bird has been around for many hundreds of years – a 'furry' chicken was documented by Marco Polo during his 13th Century explorations of China. Trade routes set up between the East and West brought the Silkie to Europe and, in Belgium, it was reported that the birds were once exhibited as the product of crossing a chicken with a rabbit!

Even though the Silkie is classed as a 'large fowl', it's not a large bird and is officially classified in the poultry standards as a 'light, soft-feathered' breed. The first breed standard was established in 1925, and then revised in 1993, when the bantam version was brought into the fold.

There's quite a bit of difference between the male and female birds, although both share the same fundamentally broad, rounded body shape that's cloaked in a mass of fluffy feathers. It's the hens which have the fluffier, more pronounced appearance and, although they don't share the male's larger, mulberry-coloured, cushion-type comb and wattles, their crest feathering is much finer and more

The Silkie makes a great 'back garden' bird, although its profuse feathering means muddy, wet conditions can pose a bit of a problem

pompom-like. The male's head feathering is rather more spikey, with longer, thinner feathers slanting rearwards at a rakish angle.

The tails are another obvious, distinguishing feature. The male's is a fairly ragged, untidy affair, but things are much neater on the female. A much larger cushion ensures that most of the tale's shape is lost on the female, engulfed in a soft mass of the silkiest feathers. These hens can almost look Cochinesque about the body.

When viewed from the side, a good Silkie should appear stout, short-backed and be showing minimal feathered leg (especially in the female). The neck is profusely hackled on both sexes, the breast is full and rounded and the shoulders square. Rather like the male's tail, the wings – when spread – have a ragged appearance to them, particularly the tips of the flight

feathers which hang down in a series of straggles.

The head, while obviously dominated in both sexes by the feathery crest, also features black eyes, a short, dark beak and mulberry-coloured face. The ear lobes should ideally be a bright shade of turquoise blue, but a similar colour to the rest of the head gear is permitted. The legs, which should be blue, are moderately feathered, as are the middle and outer toes on each foot.

There are just five standardised colours of Silkie; black, blue, gold, white and partridge. The white and the black are self-explanatory, and are probably the most popular colours among exhibitors. The blue and the gold are relatively straightforward too, being even blue and bright gold respectively. The partridge, however, enjoys a rather more involved colour

Female cushion feathers should be among the softest, most hair-like on the bird, and be sufficient to virtually cover the tail

scheme. On male birds the head, crest, back and shoulders are dark orange, the neck hackles are orange (with a central, black stripe). There's black in the wing primaries and tail, on the breast and on the legs and feet.

On the female, the neck and breast feathers are black with a lemon stripe, the hackles are black with lemon edging and the crest is a lemon and black mixture. The rest of the feathering is soft partridge brown with black barring, the undercolour is slate grey and some black is permissible in the tail.

Important choices

As with an increasing number of pure breeds these days, buying good Silkies is becoming harder, so it's important to do your research, contact the club and locate a respected breeder to buy from, based on knowledgeable recommendation. One of the most important things to note is that this breed is susceptible to Marek's disease, which is a killer. It's an unpleasant condition that affects the bird's nerve endings, leading to the formation of cancerous tumours, paralysis and eventual death. There is a vaccination available called Poulvac, although

A good wing, illustrating the ragged yet soft nature of the feathers you would hope to find. Conventional, stiff, primary-type feathers here should be avoided

Legs and feet should be blue, and free from roughness and crusting. Raised scales are a sign of scaly leg mite

at the time of writing it is only available from one source in the UK, Southampton-based Fort Dodge Animal Health (tel: 01489 781711). The vaccination is a once-only treatment, but it must be administered within the first three weeks of a bird's life. However, its use represents a controversial issue within the Silkie Club; the camp is divided. While it doesn't offer a 100% guarantee of immunity from the effects of Marek's, some regard it as an important treatment for their birds.

Not all breeders are prepared to run to the expense of vaccinating all the birds they hatch, so this is an important question you need to ask any potential seller. If the answer is at all vague, then you'd perhaps be wise to simply walk away. Vaccinated birds are probably the safest bet for new domestic keepers. Some breeders set themselves the task of attempting to breed-out the problems, but it seems that very few have enjoyed much success with this.

One of the problems is that Marek's disease doesn't always show itself immediately; it can lay dormant in a bird. Typically it'll be triggered by an increased level of stress, such as that caused by a hen coming into lay, or possibly by having its routine upset following purchase. Also, it doesn't always develop into the full-blown disease, and has been known to cause blindness in birds only moderately affected.

Another purchase point to consider if you're serious about the birds you're buying, is their colour. The recent growth in popularity of the breed (particularly the bantam version) among hobby keepers, has proved somewhat of a double-edged sword. While awareness of the Silkie has grown usefully, so has the idea that money can be made from selling these cuddly birds to unwary beginners. Hand-in-hand with this has come the desire to start breeding different, non-standard colours by crossing the established versions with all and sundry.

There is, of course, a dedicated group of serious breeders who treat their standardised strains with the care they deserve but, unfortunately, there are also increasing numbers of people willing to operate less scrupulous breeding programs in the hope of creating saleable offspring. All I can really say is 'buyer beware!'

Great character

The Silkie is a very docile breed, which makes it extremely easy to tame. It doesn't have a flighty bone in its body, which is another factor that contributes greatly to its general appeal. Containment is simple and, because these birds aren't fliers, you'll need little more than a four-foot high fence to keep them in place. Another major breed characteristic is the Silkie's legendary broodiness; it really is famous for it, and used by many poultry keepers as their resident hatching hen! It only seems to take a warming of the weather to trigger this instinct. Of course, laying performance suffers accordingly – you can't have both aspects at the same time. So, if one of your primary aims is a good supply of eggs from your poultry, then the Silkie simply isn't the breed for you. However, it's worth bearing in mind that those eggs which are produced – you'll be lucky to get more than 100 per season – have a reputation for being among the sweetest you'll ever taste. What's more, in the Far East these eggs are believed to have medicinal qualities.

One of the big potential dangers with this breed is that inexperienced keepers often fail to see when things are starting to go wrong. The profuse feathering has a lot to do with this as it can hide a multitude of parasite-related problems. Legs and heads are particularly prone to mite infestations and, with the amount of time these birds can spend on broody duty, you need to keep a very careful check on the cleanliness of the nest box too. While it's vital to inspect the head carefully for the presence of crest mite, the fine nature of the feathers, combined with the dark-coloured skin, can make this difficult for the inexperienced.

Breeding battle

As far as breeding is concerned, the Silkie can be a tricky, unpredictable proposition. Fertility varies, often for no apparent reason, so hatching

Note the startling, turquoise-blue ear lobe on this partridge hen. Mulberry lobes are also acceptable, but this 'tropical' blue is just amazing!

quality stock can be a struggle. This is one aspect of the breed which requires more experience; it's what you could describe as a 'high maintenance' breed in this respect. On the plus side, the male birds sometimes actively help the females with chick rearing, which is an interesting characteristic.

The docile nature of the Silkie means that it can be susceptible to bullying if mixed with other more aggressive breeds. Bantam versions, however, tend to be a little more

Gold Silkie bantam hen

feisty, and are quite capable of holding their own when the going gets tough! Among themselves, however, Silkies tend to make excellent pen fellows, to the extent that multiple males living together without a problem isn't unheard of in Silkie circles.

Silkies can be 'sulky' birds, and they don't like being moved from familiar surroundings.

Consequently, this can throw-up problems when buying. It's not uncommon for newly-acquired birds to stop eating and drinking, and maybe even to die, simply because of the stress and disruption caused by the change in environment. It's important to do all you can to ease the environmental transition. Talk to the breeder you're buying from and ask how they look after their birds, then do all you can to match that. Pick their brains and use their experience to help you and your new birds. Another good tip is to keep the birds' diet the same. If the seller is willing, take away some feed with the birds because at least you'll know that they'll eat that, all else being equal.

Finally, be careful not to buy your birds too young, otherwise you'll run the risk of being sold male birds. The Silkie is quite a difficult bird to sex at an early age unless you know what you're looking for and, regrettably, it's not uncommon for the less scrupulous sellers to pass-off young males as females to unsuspecting buyers. Things become clearer after 12-14 weeks, with the male's generally thicker-set features, larger headgear and swept-back crest feathering becoming more obvious.

YES OR NO?

✔ Fantastic plumage.
✔ Family-friendly.
✔ Engaging character.
✔ Great show bird.

✘ Chicks vulnerable.
✘ Infertility problems.
✘ Not a great layer.
✘ Feathering hides problems

Sussex

All you could want from a chicken; performance, practicality, ease of ownership and great appearance too

Buying top quality chickens, whatever the breed, is a skill born out of experience. It takes a practised eye to pick good from bad and unfortunately it's an ability that only develops with time. However, you can tip the odds of getting it right much more in your favour by only dealing with established and recommended breeders (preferably suggested to you via the relevant breed club). It's something we would stress a lot, because it's a vital issue.

If you choose to buy from a livestock auction or sale, you're taking a risk. Typically, you'll be buying a feathery unknown quantity which might turn out to be OK, or it might not. Source your new birds from a specialist breeder, on the other hand and, although you'll pay a bit more, the chances are that you'll get good advice and quality stock – these suppliers have their reputations to think of, after all.

Sourcing a Sussex

Although the Sussex isn't classified as a rare breed, some of the colour varieties are quite difficult to source nowadays. Most popular of the lot is the light, with its very attractive black and white feathering. This was the variety which was developed as the main commercial layer, and there are still strains available today. Other colours – in order of popularity – include speckled, buff, white, red, silver and brown. All of these are much rarer than the light.

Because the breed was developed over a very long period as a dual-purpose, utility bird it has many advantages for the domestic keeper who is interested in both a supply of good quality, well-sized eggs, and tasty meat. The bird's laying performance arose because it was essentially a farmer's fowl in the old days, so the ability to produce a useful number of eggs before the hens were fattened was a valuable extra attraction.

Of course, like most other breeds, the Sussex has attracted attention from exhibition enthusiasts over the years. Thankfully, though, its practical, utility roots haven't been too badly eroded by showmen striving for their perception of the ideal exhibition bird. So, while today's show strains tend to present better feathering and size than the more commercial strains, both options will still produce 180-220 eggs in a season, which is pretty good by pure breed standards.

It's worth bearing in mind that genuine commercial strains

A The eye should be bold and bright, with a clearly-defined pupil and red-coloured iris. A diffuse pupil/iris boundary is something to watch for and avoid; it can be an indicator that the bird has suffered with Marek's disease.

B Combs, earlobes and wattles should be bright red on hens that are laying. Avoid birds with pale pink headgear, unless you're looking at a pullet which hasn't yet reddened-up fully. Uneven wattles won't affect laying ability, but aren't a characteristic that should be included in a breeding programme.

C The beak should be light-coloured, short and curved. Watch for twisting or other obvious deformities.

D The neck should be medium-length, essentially straight (without kinks), and sized in proportion with the rest of the body. Commercial strains often show poor hackle colouring, with too little black. Pure breeds should have solid black hackle feathers with white lacing, running around the circumference of the neck.

E The breast must be full and deep. Handle the bird and check for a crooked breast bone, and/or the presence of abscesses on the breast. The latter can be a sign of poor husbandry, and should set the alarm bells ringing.

F The thighs should be squarely set when viewed from the front with plenty of width between them – ideally a hands-width. Narrowness here will certainly inhibit egg production, and is a bad feature.

G The shanks (the scaly part of the leg) should be short and white, with good, thick bone. They must also be free from feathers. Feet with five instead of four toes indicate a lack of breed purity, as does leg feathering. Feet should also show good, tight scales – no roughness or raised scabs (scaly leg). Pullets have much tighter leg scales than hens, which is a good age indicator.

H Wings should be held tight and centrally against the body, not hanging down loosely. Avoid birds with a 'split wing', evident when the wing is spread to reveal a pronounced step between the primary and secondary feathers.

I Look for plenty of space from vent to hock, so that there is no constriction of the egg-laying organs. The more space there is, the greater the likelihood of the hen being a good layer.

J A clean backside is always a good indicator of a healthy bird that's been well cared for.

K The tail should run in line with the neck, when viewed from above. It shouldn't be held to the right or left (what's called a 'wry tail'). While this isn't a particular problem from a laying point of view, it is if you're trying to breed because it's gene-related.

L The body as a whole must be big and broad with a flat back. The latter was a feature included to ensure that the bird sits squarely on the plate. Male birds should have the appearance of a breeze block, with rounded-off edges! Skin should be white.

M Look for a round head (when viewed from the side). Avoid 'crow-faced' birds with long beaks and shallow, pointed faces. Ideally the bird should have sleek, tight feathering around the head; it shouldn't be puffed-up. A good Sussex should present a generally bright, alert and friendly character.

will always be smaller and less 'showy' than the exhibition fowl. A really good laying hen doesn't waste its energy on fancy feathering or getting too large. All effort is put into the production of the large eggs, and plenty of them! So if you decide to opt for out-and-out laying performance, you will get larger eggs than those from an exhibition-type Sussex, but you can't expect to have the ultimate in looks as well.

Practical pointers

The Sussex really is a bird for all keepers. Whether you're an experienced fancier or an enthusiastic novice, the breed has something to offer.

Their generally placid nature means that these birds are perfectly happy to be kept in confinement assuming, of course, that they aren't overcrowded, and that they don't get bored. Let's face it, bored birds are trouble, whatever the breed. So if you're going to keep them in, then put them on deep litter and make sure they've got plenty to keep them amused (scratch feed, hanging cabbages etc). Birds that are bored, or housed with insufficient room, will quickly start to develop bad habits, like egg-eating, feather-pecking or bullying.

Assessing birds is a subjective business, and experience is a great help. These birds are the same age, but the buff is the better bet, with its broader shoulders and 'tighter' wings – important Sussex characteristics

LARGE OR SMALL?

There are probably more light bantams around these days than there are large fowl. We're not aware of any brown or red bantams, but all the others exist in reasonable numbers. Huge numbers of light Sussex bantams were kept in back gardens during WWII – it proved an ideal utility-type bird.

The bantams lay as well as the large fowl, although the eggs are obviously smaller. They make great broodies too – gamekeepers used to love them for rearing partridge. Of the large fowl, the exhibition strains tend to lay a smaller egg than the commercial types.

A bird showing signs of being 'crow-faced', with its longish beak and slightly narrow, pinched face. Best avoided!

From this angle you can see that the buff has a better, more rounded head, and that the light's eye looks somewhat sunken and pale

Conversely, they love to free-range too; they're an active breed which loves to keep busy. But be warned that their enthusiastic activities can be destructive too, as far as formal garden planting is concerned. So it's advisable to restrict their free-ranging to the 'rougher' areas of your garden! Their active nature also has a relevance to feeding. Birds which don't get enough exercise, and are given too much to eat, will run to fat. Not only is this bad for their overall health, but it'll hinder laying performance too, so this should be avoided.

The placid side of the Sussex's nature helps ensure that the hens make excellent and attentive broodies and mothers. Some believe that bantam versions are better at this than the large fowl and, being a good deal lighter, they're certainly less clumsy.

Finally, the breed is classified as 'heavy', so it's more of a flutterer than a flyer. Nevertheless, they will manage to get over a three-foot fence or hedge, so you'll need to install something double this height to keep these birds securely contained – a five or six foot fence will suffice.

Perhaps the ideal light Sussex hen; great head, beak, eye and hackle. She's almost smiling for the camera, too!

HISTORY IN A NUTSHELL

- The Sussex is a traditional, old English breed that was developed over generations as a utility bird; producing eggs and meat.
- Provided the lynchpin of the Sussex fattening industry from the 1850s onwards, centred around the East Sussex towns of Heathfield and Uckfield, and supplying the London markets.
- Sussex Poultry Club formed in 1903, in Lewes.
- Red, light and speckled were the first varieties recognised.
- Speckled is the most original variety.
- Light is said to have been created by crossing Cochin, Brahma and Dorking. It was developed into one of the world's premier breeds, with commercial strains being among the best layers of their time.
- Buff and white varieties arrived in the 1920s.
- White offered impressive commercial laying performance too.
- The silver was created in the 1940-50s, by Captain Duckworth.

YES OR NO?

✔ Great, placid nature
✔ Family-friendly breed
✔ Good range of colours
✔ Very practical for eggs and meat
✔ Easy to handle
✔ Loves to free-range
✔ Flutterer, not a flyer
✔ Hens make food broodies

✘ Males touchy during mating season
✘ Most colours tricky to source
✘ Will become fat if overfed

Wyandotte

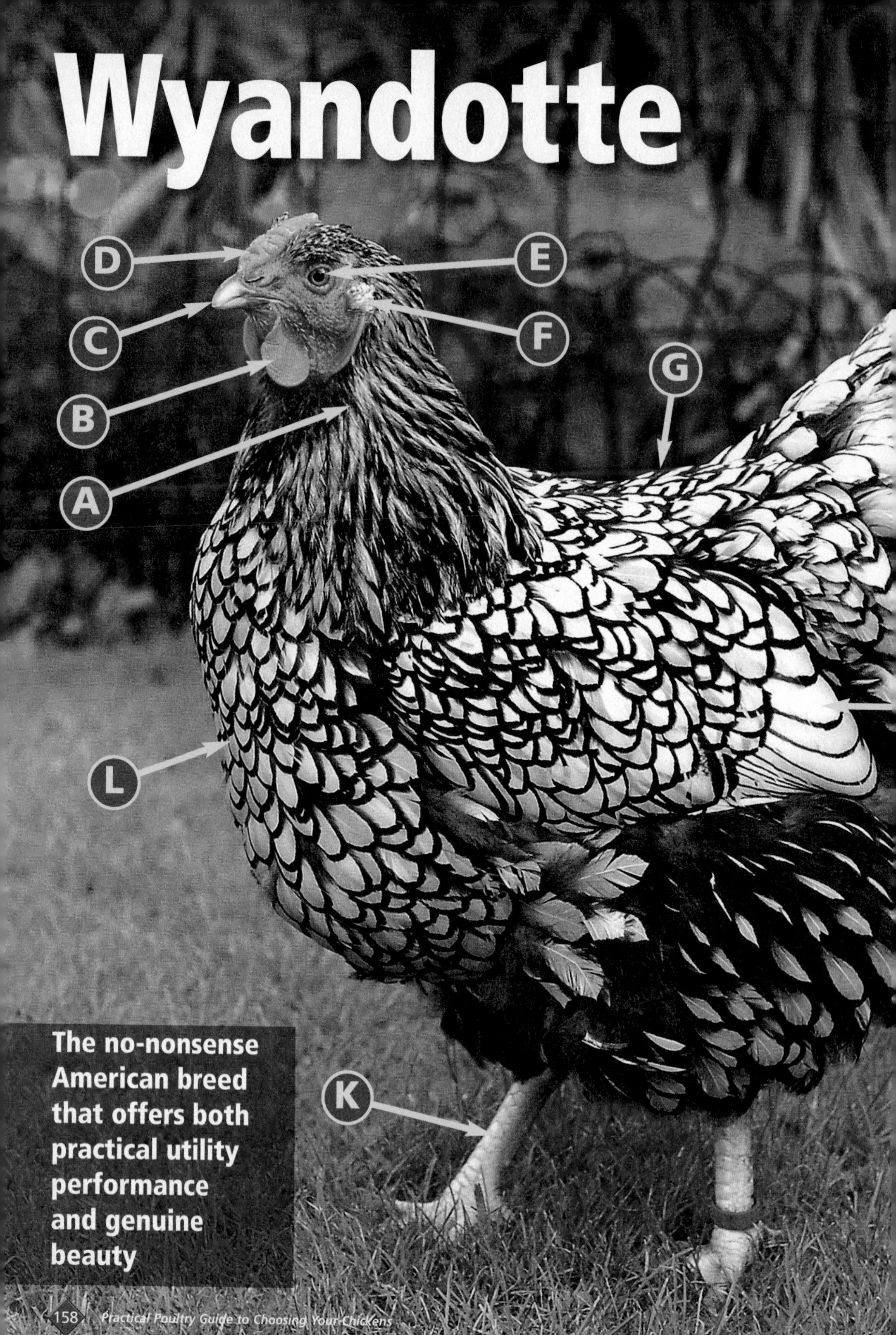

The no-nonsense American breed that offers both practical utility performance and genuine beauty

D
C
B
A
E
F
G
L
K

A The ideal Wyandotte neck will be medium length, attractively curved and well hackled.

B Wattle size can vary, depending on strain. Some breeders prefer longer rather than shorter. The standard calls for medium length.

C The beak should be stout and curved, but its colour varies. On pencilled or laced examples it should be horn-coloured, on blacks with dark undercolour it will be black with yellow patching while, with all other plumage colours it should be bright yellow. Note that the latter tends to become diluted towards the end of the laying season.

D Short but broad head must feature a rose comb with a leader that actually curves downwards to follow the line of the head on both male and female birds. Fly-away combs are best avoided from aesthetic and/or exhibition points of view. The comb should also show 'fine workings' on top – a good number of small, rounded points. Avoid any 'dishing' of the comb, where it extends out at the front, over the beak. Combs that are too big will become mis-shapen as the bird ages.

E The eye should be bright bay (reddish-brown) in all plumage colours. Green or pale-coloured eyes (often associated with pale legs) are best avoided.

F Avoid any signs of white or yellow in the ear lobe. Texture of these, and the wattles, should be fine and smooth.

G The Wyandotte is often described as a 'bird of curves' – it should appear noticeably rounded and curvy whether you're looking at it from above, behind or from the side. The back should be broad but short, with a good rise up to the base of the tail.

H The female tail should be reasonably upright and open; the shape of an inverted 'V' when viewed from behind. Some breeders have strayed away from this to produce hens with Pekin-like tails, which lack the distinction required by the breed standard.

I The wings should be tightly tucked into the side of the body and held horizontally so that the tip almost touches the base of the tail. Avoid those seen to be drooping. Check for split wings too by spreading the wing and looking for the tell-tale 'break' between the primary and secondary feathers.

J Fluffiness around the vent area tends to be most apparent on whites, although it will be present on other colours to some degree. It's perfectly acceptable as long as it's not excessive. The danger with too much is that the feathering can extend to the ground and the legs are lost, producing an almost Orpington-like appearance. Partridge is probably the least fluffy of all the Wyandotte colours.

K Generally, legs should be bright yellow. As in this case, though, a hen's legs (and beak colour) can fade towards the end of the laying season – pigment gets used up in the yolks. So don't necessarily be put off by this. Also, birds which have been kept indoors tend not to show such bright yellow as those which are allowed to free-range.

L The Wyandotte's body should be short, deep and round, with a prominent, full breast and straight keel bone. Avoid birds showing a 'cut-away' breast.

The Wyandotte, supposedly named after the Wyandot native American people from Ohio, endured a stuttering start to life during the late 1880s. There's much debate about how the breed actually came into being and, as is so often the case, the nature of the way in which the early examples were produced means that definitive breeding records have long since disappeared.

Plenty of contradictory stories have been published over the years detailing assorted breed combinations that were ostensibly used to create the first Wyandotte, which was the silver laced version. Depending on what you read, breeders used Cochin, Brahma, Hamburgh, Poland and Sebright stock (in various combinations), as their building blocks.

However, perhaps one of the most authoritative accounts of the breed's early development, can be found in Lewis Wright's famous *Wright's Book of Poultry*. In it, he suggests that the fledgling 'Wyandotte' made its first appearance in 1873, when it was then known as the American Cochin. Reports indicated that it had been produced by crossing the Cochin with the silverspangled Hamburgh and, mysteriously, 'other blood'!

Twisted roots

Contemporary illustrations showed an exaggeratedly well-laced bird with clean legs and a rose comb featuring a Hamburgh-like leader (unlike today's birds which have a down-turned leader that follows the line of the head). But the new breed failed to catch on. It was rejected by the American Standards Committee in 1876, and it took a further four years of breeding before they tried again.

In 1880, the publicity started again, featuring a large, laced bird that, reportedly, was the result of a cross between a Hamburgh and a Brahma – with the latter being the likely source of the downward-facing comb leader. It's at this point that Poland may also have entered the fray. The breed was finally standardised in America – as the Wyandotte – in 1883.

The first examples arrived in the UK just a year or so later, and were introduced at the Staffordshire Show in 1884. Fanciers here took to the breed immediately, and wasted little time in setting about improving its lacing and ground colour. Alternative colours soon followed, with the gold laced arriving first, then the white, black and partridge. The blue and buff laced, first seen here in 1897, were created by crossing the gold laced version with the white. The white had originated from sports of the silver laced variety, and was bred in America specifically for its laying ability. This was done very successfully, and the bird developed into one of the best commercial layers ever. At one time, it held laying records in both America and the United Kingdom.

Good looker

The attractive Wyandotte is known for its curvaceous body; it's short and deep with a full breast. The saddle is wide and sweeps up to a fairly upright tail.

The bird's head is short but broad (linking the breed with its Brahma parentage), with a curved yellow or horn-coloured beak,

Hen head detail illustrating neat comb 'workings' and beautifully red headgear

Not such a good example; this black shows white in the ear lobe, a slightly fly-away comb leader and lightish eye colour

Yellow legs are a must-have feature on a good Wyandotte

prominent bay coloured eyes, and bright red rose comb, smooth red ear lobes and average-sized wattles. The neck is of medium length and features plenty of hackle feathers on male birds.

Legs are of medium length too, with the thighs well-feathered but the shanks clean and ideally bright yellow (this colour can become diluted on laying hens). Yellow colouring extends to the skin too, which stood the Wyandotte in very good stead as a table bird in the States. However, this was more of a limiting factor in the UK, where whiteskinned fowl were preferred.

Many plumage colours are now available, and 15 of them have been standardised by the Poultry Club of Great Britain. White remains the most popular among exhibitors but, from the backyard keeper's point of view, it's the spectacular laced or partridge examples that really turn heads. However, good Wyandottes are becoming harder to find these days, particularly if you're after large fowl. The number of breeders producing top quality stock is currently on the decline.

AT A GLANCE

Size
Large (large fowl and bantam)

Origin
America

Weights
Male – not less than 4.08kg (9lbs)
Female – 3.17kg (7lbs)

Egg laying
160+ pa

Colours
Barred, Black, Blue, Buff, Columbian, Partridge, Silver pencilled, Red, White, Silver laced, Gold laced, Blue laced, Buff laced

Post-moult 'mossiness' which appears in the ground colour may be a problem on a silver laced bird from a show point of view, but it's also a sign of a good layer – a bird producing eggs well into its moult

Partridge male; the 'traditional' colouring

The many colour options have led to a plethora of clubs being formed over the years. Currently there are five distinct organisations, but the first was the Laced Wyandotte Club. To begin with this was known as the Silver Laced Wyandotte Club, but this name became limiting as more laced colours were created and brought into the fold. There's also the Partridge & Pencilled Club (including blue versions of each), the Black Wyandotte Club, the White Wyandotte Club and, finally, the Wyandotte Club, catering for any versions that don't have a specific club of their own. As you might imagine, the White and the Laced clubs are the two strongest.

Careful choice

So, having decided on the colour you fancy, the best thing is to consult the relevant club for advice on a recommended supplier. Wyandottes do, of course, come up in livestock sales and auctions but, unless it's a specialist event, we'd advise the inexperienced to steer clear of this purchase method. The danger is that these sales can be used by less scrupulous breeders to offload their sub-standard stock on to unsuspecting and/or ill-informed buyers. So, tempting as the idea of getting a bargain may seem, you'd really do well to resist the idea, and seek out an experienced and proven breeder instead.

Prices can vary enormously. The many different colours can have a distinct effect on desirability, so it's very hard to generalise about what you'll have to pay. Laced, Partridge and Pencilled birds tend to command the greatest prices, simply because the majority regard them as the most attractive. Trios have been known to make £200 (2009 prices) at a top sale whereas, at the other end of the scale, birds can cost as little as £10 each.

From a practical point of view, the Wyandotte is a usefully hardy breed, and is tolerant of most climatic conditions. Its low, rose-style comb means that heat loss under cold conditions isn't nearly as bad as it can be with large, single-combed breeds such as the Leghorn.

With a placid and friendly character, the breed soon becomes

Columbian bantams are an attractive Wyandotte colour option

a favourite among keepers, and bullying shouldn't normally be an issue you need to worry about. However, it's worth being aware that the silver laced variety can be prone to feather pecking (often the pullets doing it to the cockerels!) if overcrowded at the rearing stage. For this reason, silver laced are best reared in small groups, if you have the facilities to do so. Of course, over-crowding is a basic mistake you should guard against whatever sort of poultry you keep.

Despite being a generally docile breed, the Wyandotte isn't what you might describe as a silly chicken; it tends not to do the stupid things that others might. They're not flighty either, so fencing shouldn't be a great issue, although the bantams can be somewhat more adventurous given the chance. The Wyandotte really is an easy breed to keep, with no special requirements necessary over and above all the usual good husbandry and welfare-related basics. They will happily co-exist in a mixed flock if that's what you want, but are no pushovers if tempers flare; the blacks tend to be the most dominant of all the colours.

The white Wyandotte became a utility legend both here and in America. Today, though, exhibition strains tend to show more fluffiness of feathering than the other colours

Flock development

If you really take to the Wyandotte, and decide that you'd like to start breeding your own birds, then there's good and bad news. In simple terms, the Wyandotte is a relatively easy bird to breed. Chicks tend to be robust and grow strongly but, as is so often the case with pure breeds of poultry, overall success is going to be fundamentally controlled by strain. If your birds have come from a specialist, exhibition-type flock that's had little fresh blood introduced over the years, then fertility levels may well suffer (an inevitable consequence of in-breeding).

Also, if you're hoping to breed for the show pen, then it's as well to appreciate from the outset that this is no easy task, especially if you fancy your chances with any of the laced varieties. With lacing quality accounting for 35% of the available points, getting this right is fundamental for a show bird, as is the uniformity of its ground colour. The self-colours represent a somewhat easier prospect as potential show birds, essentially because of the simplicity of their feather colouring, with type and undercolour coming more to the fore.

Proud black male displaying good breast, short back, desirable 'workings' on his comb and the important beetle-green sheen on his feathers

The white Wyandotte, developed over the years as the showman's favourite, is now appreciably different from the sort of pure utility strain found 50 or 60 years ago. They are much fluffier nowadays, and this is something which can actually hinder mating. Experienced breeders often resort to clipping away some of the most profuse fluffiness from around the vent area to give the male bird a better target to aim at, so to speak!

It's also useful to know that the chicks from partridge and silver laced can be reliably sexed at day-old; the males being a lighter colour. Blacks, too, show a similarly valuable difference straight out of the shell, with the male chicks having a noticeably lighter down colour on their undersides. Wyandotte hens make good and determined broodies. They can be enthusiastic and reliable sitters, although the large fowl are sometimes prone to a little clumsiness due to their size. For this reason, the bantam can make the

Buff laced male (above) is an attractive colour option, while the blue laced female bantam (right) is certainly a pretty and popular show bird

better, practical choice for natural brooding enthusiasts.

All in all then, the Wyandotte represents a fine dual-purpose option. Healthy young hens should be capable of laying 160+ attractively tinted eggs in a season and, for those so inclined, the male birds will provide a tasty roast. The breed's good level of general hardiness ensures that these birds will be tough enough to cope with most environmental conditions, assuming that their basic welfare requirements are met. As you'll have seen from the pictures here, some of the prettiest plumage colour schemes are real stunners, and the possibility of combining such an exciting appearance with a genuinely useful practical performance must surely make the Wyandotte worthy of serious consideration.

The Wyandotte makes a great backyard fowl, with its still useful dual-purpose performance offering genuine value. For some reason, the black tends to be the most dominant character

Hybrid or pure?

Dudley Mallett suggests that, contrary to popular belief within the Fancy, there's virtually no such thing as a 'pure-breed' chicken

The term 'pure breed' is a bit of a misnomer really, when applied to the range of chickens we have today. In fact, the majority of breeds now in existence have, over the centuries, been created by man, and never have existed naturally in the wild. Without getting into a Darwinian discussion, the only true pure-bred chicken worthy of the name is the Jungle Fowl (*Gallus gallus*).

Sometimes referred to as *G. gallus (domesticus)*, this bird was the first to be domesticated from the wild, and used as a source of eggs and meat across India and south-east Asia. Many variants were kept by villagers as working fowl, creating a range of sizes and colours which became peculiar to the area in which they were domesticated.

Common ancestor
It's from these domesticated Jungle Fowl that all the chickens of today descend. Keepers down the

This is a Rhode Rock

centuries have refined and crossed these birds and, by both selective and accidental breeding, have arrived at the range of poultry we know now.

This process of cross-breeding carries on within the breed clubs today, in an effort to refine or enhance fowl, or develop new and interesting colour variations. However, the Poultry Club of Great Britain imposes stringent conditions before a new breed or colour can be officially recognised (standardised). Proof is needed that any new cross-breed – for that's what they are – breeds true, that it is kept by more than one enthusiast and has been kept and recorded accurately for a number of years.

While the purists among the Fancy tend to look-on with disdain at today's commercial hybrids, the truth is that they really are no different than those birds they hail as pure-bred chickens. Most if not all the standardised breeds in the PCGB's book of British Poultry Standards were created by cross-breeding and, in many cases, the different breeds used in the development process are well documented to prove the point.

One of the downsides of creating this range of 'pure breeds' is that maintaining them to the standard means that a high degree of inbreeding is required. It's common practice that stud cock birds are 'line-bred' using a father-

to-daughter combination, and this goes on for generations. The inevitable result is that the fertility rates of both the male and female birds gradually slide. Nowadays it's common that many pure-bred hens will struggle to lay 80-90 eggs in a season, and infertility in male birds is a real problem. A classic example of this is the beautiful Buff Orpington, a pure-bred soft feather bird that's productive capacity has collapsed.

Every now and again breeders are forced to bring in a new line (fresh blood) to bolster productivity. In some cases the problems caused by inbreeding lead to such serious problems that the only option left is to cross-in another type altogether in a bid to salvage the line. So the undeniable conclusion to all this is that, in fact, not many 'pure breeds' are actually pure at all!

Hybrid roots

So what is a hybrid? Well, in simple terms, it's the offspring from the crossbreeding of different chicken breeds. Hybrid chickens are made by crossing two other breeds possessing desirable characteristics, usually with a specific, business-orientated purpose in mind. So a cross may be made to enhance laying performance, vigour, breast size, weight gain, flesh colour, egg colour, egg size and colour sex-linkage etc.

I used to produce hundreds of

The Amber is a pretty little hybrid laying hen

HYBRID BENEFITS

- 200+ eggs a year
- Coloured shells available
- Robust and hardy
- Disease resistant
- Typically vaccinated and wormed
- Usually under £20 per hen
- No broodiness to affect laying

Araucana chickens from which I selected my stock for showing. The Araucana cock bird carries the true, blue egg gene, particularly the black variety. My local commercial breeder used to buy my excess male birds, and used them in a breeding program to establish a hybrid, blue egg-laying hen that produced eggs in the right numbers, and of the desired colour to suit the demands of his supermarket customers. It's likely that he crossed a white egg-laying hybrid (based on the Leghorn) with my black Araucana males to avoid diluting the blue shell pigment.

The meat industry utilises hybrids with the large Indian Game in their ancestry, to maximise the size of the bird's breast. This, combined with heavy weight gain, are among the most desirable points the poultry industry seeks of its meat birds. As a result, these birds are ready for slaughter in just 12 weeks.

With all this in mind, it's clear that many in the Fancy who champion the virtues of popular and sought-after purebreeds such as the Sussex, Rhode Island Red, Plymouth Rock and Jersey Giant, are misinformed as far as the purity of these breeds is concerned. To illustrate the point, let's consider the Rhode Island Red.

This breed was created in Adamsville, USA. One of the 'building blocks' used was the black-breasted red Malay cock, which had been imported from England. This infusion gave the breed its size, disease resistance, essentially docile nature and superior meat qualities. In 1925 the Rhode Island Red Club of America donated funds for an elegant monument to the bird in Adamsville (now on the National Register of Historic Places). But a competing monument to the breed was erected by the state in 1954,

The Light Sussex was a fine utility fowl in its day, but now even a cracking example like this one would be eclipsed by a modern hybrid when it comes to egg-laying

suggesting that it had been created not for the poultry fanciers, but for the many farmers who reared it commercially in the area. So, not much breed purity there then!

The Plymouth Rock, often called simply a 'Rock' or 'Barred Rock' (after the most popular colour), is another breed that originated in the United States. It was developed in New England during the early 1800s by crossing Dominiques and Black Javas. The objective was to create a dual-purpose fowl, valued both for its meat and the hens' egg-laying ability. Much of the

development work is believed to have been carried out by John C Bennett (1804-1867) and, as with the RIR, the development story rather destroys any idea about purity of breed.

Land of the Giants

There's a similar story behind the black Jersey Giant, created by John and Thomas Black during the late 1800s in Burlington County, New Jersey. The birds varied in colour to begin with, as most effort was focussed on developing a good size and confirmation, to ensure a good-

sized roasting bird. Heavy breeds such as Black Java, Black Langshan and Dark Brahma were all mixed in to create the first examples.

Finally, the Sussex was created in the county of the same name more than a century ago, by crossing four separate breeds. The original plumage colours were brown, red, and speckled, but these were followed the light, buff and silver. The most recent variety – re-created after being lost, is the Coronation Sussex.

The breed was prized as a table fowl and the Light Sussex proved a

The Bluebelle is a very popular hybrid too; it's easy to see why!

favourite and successful competitor in the laying trials of the 1930s. Today, the Sussex is a popular breed for both exhibitors and the backyard keeper. It's made a huge contribution to the poultry industry, and is one of the ancestors of the modern broiler. As such it represents one of the oldest breeds that we have today but was, nevertheless, created by commercial breeders!

So there you have it, most birds are crossbreeds of one sort or another! Rather than bore you with the origin of the chicken species; those who turn up their noses at the thought of keeping hybrid birds are clearly missing an important point. The chicken breeds the Fanciers slavishly keep and dearly love were, in the most part, the hybrids of the 1920s and 1930s.

Fit for purpose?

The first question that any prospective poultry keeper should ask themselves is what they're intending to keep their birds for? If you can answer this question then the choice of the type of bird to keep is made simpler.

If your aim is to exhibit poultry – competing in the many PCGB-sponsored shows held all round the country – you'll need to buy the best pure-bred stock you can from a recognised and specialist breeder.

These experts will have selectively bred their birds for the show bench, meaning that they'll offer the best possible starting point for the exhibition novice.

However, if your intentions are rather more practical, and egg laying performance is important to you, then it's worthwhile appreciating that the traditional pure-breeds are generally less robust, and don't offer the same laying potential as the modern hybrid utility breeds. I often make the comparison with mongrel and pedigree dogs; the pedigree breeds can be highly-strung and not terribly robust, while a good old mongrel will usually go

There are many poultry breeders and keepers who continue to believe that the so-called 'pure breeds' that we have today are just that. In fact, even the most established, like this White Sussex, are man-made creations just like the modern hybrids

on for years! Hybrid birds are typically rugged, easy to keep and they offer excellent laying potential. They're also very pretty birds for the back garden enthusiast, and can make great family pets thanks to their docile nature.

Of course, many of the pure breeds are exceedingly handsome too, but often they can't deliver in the productivity stakes. If you're looking to keep birds for meat, the chances are you'd be doubly disappointed with a pure-bred, as many such breeds are scrawny and thin compared to the much more affordable and quicker-maturing speciality hybrid meat birds.

While some of the traditional dual-purpose breeds may have been thought satisfactory 70 years ago, few can argue that they compare favourably with today's modern hybrid alternative. Of course, there are certainly advantages in eating your own pure breed birds, in terms of the excellent flavour they offer and the peace of mind that comes from having reared them yourself and knowing that they are unadulterated. However, most families, if served up a roast Light Sussex chicken, would be horrified at the skinny offering placed in front of them.

Another misconception that I should correct is that hybrid birds are aggressive and spiteful. This simply isn't true. If they are housed well and treated with appropriate levels of husbandry so that their health and welfare is assured, then you won't have a problem. After all, if you subjected a Light Sussex to the sort of restrictive conditions found inside a battery unit, it too would become spiteful and cannibalistic.

There's no doubt in my mind that, given the right conditions and a common-sense approach, hybrid hens can represent every bit as attractive an option as their pure-bred alternatives. What's more, with purchase prices being lower, maintenance costs the same and egg production levels significantly higher, the arguments stack-up noticeably in their favour on practical grounds.

So don't look down your nose at the hybrid hen; as a productive and enjoyable back garden bird it really is hard to beat.

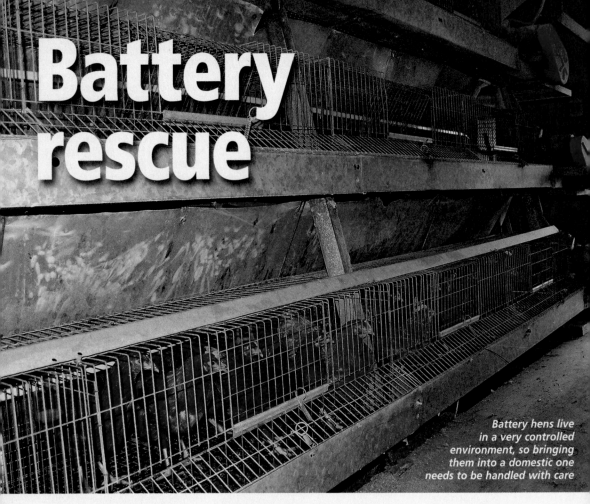

Battery rescue

Battery hens live in a very controlled environment, so bringing them into a domestic one needs to be handled with care

Terry Beebe takes a practical look at the ups and downs of living with ex-battery hens

I've watched with interest as the Battery Hen Welfare Trust has established itself in the UK. The work this charity does is quite amazing and, although there's been a bit of criticism from some quarters, I believe the whole project has helped significantly to generate an interest in poultry among a whole sector of the population who might otherwise never have become involved.

It's really heart-warming to see the concern that an ever-increasing number of people have for the plight of these ex-battery farming birds. Although those rescued only count for a tiny percentage of the national commercial flock, I believe it's the effort and commitment to save as many as possible that counts for a great deal.

Think first

However, it's also very important that new owners don't get carried away with the euphoria of the whole experience. It can be all too easy to get drawn into the battery hen rescue idea on a wave of good intention, and overlook some of the more practical considerations involved. So let's run through some of the basics relating specifically to the health and welfare of these birds, post-rescue.

The first thing to appreciate is that these hybrid hens are specialist creatures that have been developed and bred for a specific purpose. From the day they are hatched to the point they are slaughtered, they are fed and watered automatically. They are also treated with various antibiotics, and

vaccinated against a wide range of poultry diseases, to ensure they remain as healthy and productive as possible. However, this vaccination program in itself can pose a problem if rescued hens are mixed in with an existing flock of unvaccinated chickens. This is because the battery hens will, in most cases, be carrying low levels of the diseases against which they have been vaccinated. For this reason they are known as 'carriers' and they can present a health risk to other domestically-reared fowl.

Consequently, it's very important to keep a close eye on the general health of all your birds following the introduction of rescued hens. You should remain vigilant for a few weeks at least, until you're sure that all is well. If you don't have

Many new owners are shocked by how decrepit rescued hens can look

any other birds then this problem won't arise. However, don't let this disease risk put you off having rescued birds; all problems can easily be overcome.

Getting started

Organisations like the BHWT take great care to ensure that the rescued birds it distributes to new owners are in good condition; those which are under the weather are retained at the rescue centre, and allowed to convalesce. But this doesn't mean that your new birds can instantly be put outside to fend for themselves. Remember that most battery hens will have led extremely 'sheltered' lives, never having seen daylight, eaten off the ground or scratched around in the

earth for grubs. So the big wide world is a daunting and potentially frightening prospect, and newly-rescued hens must be eased into their new surroundings with care and consideration.

Don't expect new birds to adjust quickly either. I've known cases where hens put into a shed, with good light, plenty of space and an open pop hole haven't dared venture outside for up to a week. In some instances we've actually resorted to lifting them out by hand, but always find that, once out, they really enjoy the freedom they discover.

Another aspect which many new owners find surprising (judging by the number of phone calls I get) is how bad the birds can look. Lots of

new, inexperienced owners are shocked by the apparently poor condition of the hens they get. Most will have suffered from feather pecking and general feather loss and, in fact, some will appear to be almost bald. Don't worry, though; the feathers will all grow back again and, with the right care and attention, they'll soon look quite normal and as attractive as ever!

The actual feather replacement does take time – in some cases up to six weeks. In my experience, one of the best ways to help the birds through this stressful time is to add vitamins to their diet. Their bodies are working hard to replace the lost feathers, and this requires plenty of calcium and extra energy. Vitamins are easy and cheap to buy, and should form an essential part of your poultry first-aid kit. There are several well-known treatments available, including Poultry Spice and Battles Poultry Drink. Your choice is governed essentially by whether you want to add the treatment to the birds' feed or their drinking water.

Another aspect of the birds' appearance which may bother the new keeper is that some of them may well have had their beaks trimmed. In certain cases they will have been 'de-beaked' – the upper beak is cut shorter then the lower one to prevent feather pecking and egg eating. Although this may look odd, it has little effect on a bird's ability to eat and drink. Also, given time, the beaks will often re-grow.

Dealing with newly-acquired ex-battery hens is as much about good old-fashioned common sense as looking after any other sort of poultry. Just don't rush things; give them time to settle, ensure they have clean, well ventilated and dry housing, and don't turn out part-feathered birds if the weather is cold. Allow them to establish themselves happily and these hens will reward you with a good supply of tasty eggs for breakfast!

Feeding

I'm also asked often about how best to feed ex-battery birds. Well, these birds, being used to conveyer belt-supplied feed and nipple-type drinkers, often don't recognise the sort of feeders and drinkers that

Battery hens are pushed to the limit when 'in service', so don't expect 300+ eggs a season from rescued birds

most backyard keepers use. So I suggest it's sensible to shake a little feed on to the floor once they are in the house, and gently spill a little water to give them the idea of where the food and water is, then leave them to their own devices. Don't wet the floor, or scatter too much food, as this will attract other visitors such as rats and mice.

Personally I use layers pellets, but a good quality mash will be OK too. You can also add a little wheat, but only as a treat. If you want eggs, then feed the birds what they need to produce these for you. Stick to a professional, balanced feed product, and add feed treats such as cabbage, fresh fruit, mixed corn and bread (small amounts) in sensible quantities only. My own birds love apples, which are another great dietary supplement.

Water is easy to supply, and there are a large number of properly designed drinkers on the market. Bowls can be used, although they tend to get polluted by droppings and litter from the floor, so are more of an effort to keep clean. A constant supply of fresh, clean drinking water is absolutely essential for all poultry.

Try to cover drinkers and feeders if you can and, ideally, keep the feeder in the hen house. This will help prevent rodents and wild birds helping themselves, reducing the risks of disease and wastage. It also encourages the birds to return in the evening for their last feed of the day.

Precious plants?

Once the birds are settled into their new surroundings, it won't take long for them to become very tame. This is what most people want from these birds; pets and egg-layers... what a great combination! One word of warning, though. If you are a keen gardener, or if you already have an ornamental garden, then you must think about protecting the precious areas from the hens with some form of fencing. All breeds of poultry dig, and ex-battery hybrids are no exception. Given the chance, these hens clear an area of all forms of plant life in a very short space of time. They are just like little JCBs on legs!

Allow new birds plenty of time to settle inside after the move. Also be aware of the disease risk if mixing with an existing flock

The birds will quickly establish a favourite patch of soil where they will take a dust bath – the natural way they treat themselves against parasites. This can be anything up to two feet across, and will be in an area where the soil is very dry and fine. Dust-bathing is a very important activity for hens but, even if you see them doing it regularly, you'll still need to keep a close watch on their condition for yourself. Handle them all regularly to inspect for signs of the most common parasites (lice and mites). It's sensible to give them all a good shake of anti-louse powder just to be on the safe side.

While on the subject of parasites, it's also good practice to worm your birds on a regular basis. The move to a new environment

Given adequate time, care and attention, ex-battery hens make ideal pets for the novice keeper

may promote this problem and, if you're in any doubt, contact your local vet.

Hybrids, such as the ISA Brown (this is a trade name for a battery hen, although the name does change subject to the breeder or supplier), are actually a cross between a Rhode Island Red and a Light Sussex. They are fantastic layers and are among the easiest of all poultry breeds to keep and manage. They are what's classed as 'low maintenance', although you shouldn't imagine for a minute that this means they don't actually need to be looked after, because they certainly do. But, unlike some of the speciality pure breeds, they don't have any specific husbandry needs that make them more difficult for the novice keeper to cope with.

The same rules apply to these birds as for all poultry – cleanliness and good quality feed are essential. General checking for fleas, red mite and a regular worming should be just about all that's required to keep both you and the birds happy. Finally, though, always remember where the birds have come from, and that they will have been laying heavily for up to 18 months or so. Give them a rest and, although the egg production may not be as plentiful as it once was, these birds are well worth the effort. •